FLOCABULARY
PRESENTS

LEVEL
BLUE

the word up!

PROJECT

D1294532

THE FLOCABULARY ARTIST TEAM

AKIR, PLAY, NETTY, REASON, RIDDICK, ESCHER, GREY, TRAJIK, 9TH WONDER, ALEX, SPECTAC, CHARLES

ISBN: 0-9768292-6-6

Lyrics and Performances by Escher, Trajik, Netty, Reason, Isaac Brody, Alex Rappaport
Music by Alex Rappaport, Ed Boyer, Jay Lifton, Sean Divine
Workbook by Bridget Weldon-Ott and Pamela Jones
Edited by Blake Harrison, Alexander Rappaport, Laura Siciliano-Rosen, Lisbeth Kaiser, and Marty Keiser
Cover Design and Layout by Bashan Aquart
Image Credits: Unit 2- World Journal Tribune photo of Muhammad Ali by Ira Rosenberg, 1967.
Unit 5 - Nydia Velázquez, official 109th Congress, 2005. Unit 8 - The Embarkation of Montgomery's troops at Crown Point drawn by Sydney Adamson ; half-tone plate engraved by J.W. Evans, 1902. Unit 12 - Mary Bowser photo by James A. Chambers, U.S. Army Deputy, Military Intelligence. Elizabeth Van Lew photo by National Park Service. All images courtesy of The Library of Congress.

Books by Flocabulary Press are available at special discounts for bulk purchases by educational institutions and programs. Please address inquiries to:

Flocabulary Press
315 W. 39th St. Suite 1610
New York, NY 10018

Or visit us online at www.flocabulary.com

the Word Up! PROJECT

Flocabulary

Hip-Hop in the Classroom

Unit 1 - The Great Escape

1A Introduction

We've all wanted to get away at one time or another. The narrator in this song faces a pretty tough life on his block, but he finds ways to escape.

1B Song Lyrics

Hey yo, Trajik.
What's up, B?
I've got to make the great escape.
Word?

It's 7 o'clock and it's time to **embark**,
And set off on my travels though it's still dark.
It's just me in the house 'cause my dad's not around,
And my mom's got to work at the hospital now.
But that's OK I **fend** for myself,
Protect myself, my health, and my friends.
And **vice versa,** they've got my back too,
Stay close like skin stays to a tattoo.

I move fast on the map like a cat, dodging trouble,
Through broken buildings and all that **rubble**.
With more rats than that movie *Ratatouille*,
The streets **teem** with rats, you hearing that?
And while they **vie** and fight for some forgotten cheese,
The biggest rat of all was eyeing me.
I ran off to school, it's a great escape,
And cut through the gangs like a razor-blade.

At home I can't even get the time of day,
But my friends are excited, they're never **blasé**.
They smile and greet me, it's quite a **reception**,
Call me creamy ranch, 'cause I'm fresh with the dressing.

Hook

Sometimes late at night, I can't even sleep,
'Cause people argue and **wrangle** in the streets.
Usually, my street is **desolate**,
There's no people around, they won't mess with it.
Most families have moved away for better schools
To increase and **augment** their safety too.
But it's not all disorder and **anarchy**,
There's a man selling gum in a stand for me.

And there is one **tract** of land, that's so attractive man,
Every time I see it I want to rap again.

And from my roof you get a wide view, a **panorama**,
It's true; we can't afford a camera.
But that's cool, because I've got the image in my mind,
I wouldn't forget the image even if I went blind.
I've made an intense, **ardent** promise
To always stay bright in the face of darkness.

So I'm on this, like lazy kids on couches.
I'm on this, like roofs on houses.
I'm on this, and I'll always stay true.
Make waves, so make way dude, I break through.

1C Words Defined

Below you'll find each vocabulary word that was used in the song. Each word is followed by the part of speech, a simple definition and a meaningful sentence. Some words will also have synonyms, antonyms and other forms of the word listed.

1. anarchy (noun) a state of lawlessness, confusion or disorder

The crowd erupted into a state of *anarchy* during the concert.
Synonyms: chaos, disorder, turmoil
Other forms: The *anarchist* (noun) lit the garbage heap on fire and soon the whole street was ablaze.

2. ardent (adj) passionate, enthusiastic and fiery

Quincy was an *ardent* fan of any sports related books or authors.
Synonyms: impassioned, fervent, zealous

3. augment (verb) to add to

Larry's dad agreed to *augment* his allowance by two dollars a week.
Synonyms: to boost, increase, enhance
Antonyms: to decrease, reduce

4. blasé (adj) unimpressed and indifferent

We all thought Ken would be really excited about the prestigious award he received, but instead he was very *blasé* about the whole thing.
Synonyms: bored, disenchanted
Antonyms: eager, enthusiastic

5. desolate (adj) without any people; dismal and devastated

We were shipwrecked and washed up on the most *desolate* island.
Other forms: *Desolate* is also a verb meaning "to devastate," as in: Several mean boys tried to *desolate* my sand castle on the beach by running through it. Something that is destroyed is an example of *desolation* (noun).

5

6. embark (verb) to start or begin

Trina is going to *embark* on a trip and sail around the world by herself.
Synonyms: to commence, launch, undertake

7. fend (verb) to ward off or defend

The rock stars had to *fend* off the screaming and swarming girls as they exited the building.
Synonyms: to repel, resist, shield

8. panorama (noun) an unobstructed or complete view

The celebrity's home had a *panorama* of the entire valley and beyond.
Other forms: The *panoramic* (adj) view from the top of the building was breathtaking.

9. reception (noun) the act or instance of receiving or meeting

The boys gave the girls a chilly *reception* at the Super Bowl party.
Other forms: A person is usually very *receptive* (adj) when someone offers to clean their bathroom and kitchen for them. .

10. rubble (noun) broken bits and pieces

After the huge earthquake, the buildings were nothing but *rubble*.
Synonyms: debris, fragments, wreckage

11. teem (verb) to swarm, brim or overflow

Ponds often *teem* with fish, insects and frogs.
Synonyms: to abound, overrun, be prolific
Antonyms: to lack, need

12. tract (noun) an area, expanse or region

While trying to buy a *tract* of land, Chris had to be taken to the hospital due to his inflamed digestive *tract*.

13. vice versa (noun) conversely, in reverse

Kristina hates the homecoming queen, and *vice versa*: The queen hates her back.

14. vie (verb) to compete for

Charlie and Big "T" are both *vying* for starting-point guard spot on the ball team.
Synonyms: to compete, contend, strive

15. wrangle (verb) to argue or dispute

Eleanor likes to *wrangle* with her father about the dangers of smoking.
Synonyms: to dispute, fight, brawl
Antonyms: to agree, give in

Unit 1

anarchy / ardent / augment / blasé / desolate / embark / fend / panorama / reception / rubble / teem / tract / vice versa / vie / wrangle

Other forms: *Wrangle* is also a noun meaning "a noisy dispute or altercation," as in: During the *wrangle*, Everett threw plates and cups at Stephanie.

1D Fix the Mistake

Each of the sentences below has a mistake. The wrong vocabulary words have been used, so the sentences don't make sense. Rewrite each sentence using the correct vocabulary word from this unit.

1. My grandpa is going to **wrangle** on a trip to Italy, Greece and Spain after he renews his passport and completes his foreign language classes.

2. Randy was such a(n) **blasé** baseball fan that he had numerous signed baseballs, jerseys, bats and pennants in a special glass cabinet in his living room.

3. Most celebrities have to **augment** off the paparazzi even as they do the most basic routines of their lives like going grocery shopping or to the gym.

4. The rescue workers had to dig through the **reception** after the earthquake to look for survivors.

5. The largest **panorama** of land was slated to have a housing development built on it by summer.

6. Our section of the stadium shouted at the opposing team's section of the stadium and **anarchy**.

7. There were four athletes **teeming** for the gold medal in the final race.

8. Maggie was so **desolate** about winning the largest lottery winnings in history that we all thought she must be in shock.

9. Sarah likes to **fend** with others in her debate class because she knows she will always win.

10. Maybe there was a hive under the slide, because the playground was **embarking** with bees.

11.   Some wedding **rubbles** are extremely fancy with jazz bands, fancy decorations, and expensive food.

        _____

12.   The **vice versa** from the top of the tallest building in the world was so amazing that I took over one hundred pictures.

        _____

13.   The military training exercise required the new recruits to be dropped off in one of the most **ardent** places in the country, and then survive for three days with only what was in their packs.

        _____

14.   Sandy got a job; she wanted some money to **vie** her allowance.

        _____

15.   **Tract** erupted in the streets when the police officers started to fire rubber bullets at the gathering crowd.

        _____

1E Pick the Winner

Circle the word that best fits into the sentence. Then write a sentence below that uses the word you didn't pick in a meaningful way.

1.   Her bookshelf revealed that she was a(n) **(ardent OR desolate)** fan of mystery books.

2.   _____

3.   The rescue dogs were trained to sniff through the **(reception OR rubble)** and signal their handlers when they located a possible survivor.

4.   _____

5.   The paparazzi were **(vying OR teeming)** around Britney Spears to get a photo of her and her children playing at the park.

6.   _____

7.   Fishermen like to **(embark OR fend)** early in the morning for the best chance at catching the most salmon.

8.   _____

anarchy / ardent / augment / blasé / desolate / embark / fend / panorama / reception / rubble / teem / tract / vice versa / vie / wrangle

9. Two of the most popular cheerleaders **(wrangled OR augmented)** over which one of them would take the handsome quarterback to the prom.

10.

_____

1F Draw the Relationships

In each grouping of eight words below, draw straight lines between the synonyms (words that mean similar things) and squiggly lines between any antonyms (words that mean nearly opposite things). Every word should have at least one line connected to it. Some may have more.

1
       blasé   embark   fend off   unimpressed

social gathering   set off

          give in   reception

2
       wrangle   desolate   decrease   swarm

populated   argue

        augment   teem

3
           tract   anarchy

unenthusiastic   region

scenic view   chaos

        panorama   ardent

4
         debris   destroyed

rubble   cooperate

vice versa   in reverse

         vie   desolate

1G Understanding What You Read

Read the passage below. Then answer the questions.

Dad was excited about the decision to <u>embark</u> on our journey to the coast by noon, because he thought we'd be there by midnight at the latest. I was a bit more <u>blasé</u> about it, thinking that, knowing how the man drives, it would take us two days no matter what time we left.

My sister, Alex, was being the typical sullen teenager. As she was letting us know, she wasn't excited at all about the prospect of a car trip with the family. In her mind, these car trips were when the family descended into <u>anarchy</u>. She would constantly <u>wrangle</u> for back seat space and I would have to <u>fend</u> her off. By the middle of the trip, I had usually decided it was just best to stare out the window at the <u>desolate</u> landscape.

There were upsides to these trips, I suppose. Mom usually would sing in the car when things got really boring. And, of course, it was always fun watching my sister argue with dad as she made some <u>ardent</u> point about her curfew being too early, or mine being too late. Regardless, it was our arrival at the coast that was the most fun. Depending on what time we did end up getting there, the <u>reception</u> we got from the friends we hadn't seen since last summer was usually the best part of all.

1. How did the narrator feel about taking the trip?
(A) excited
(B) unhappy
(C) indifferent
(D) bored

2. What does the narrator mean by "anarchy" in the second paragraph?
(A) lack of government control
(B) general chaos
(C) peaceful times
(D) violence

3. The story suggests that the family is going
(A) on a family trip
(B) to a funeral
(C) to accept an award
(D) to a sporting event

4. The "desolate landscape" in the second paragraph suggests they were traveling through
(A) a forest
(B) a beach
(C) a desert
(D) a city

5. The narrator of this story is most likely a
(A) toddler
(B) grandfather
(C) lawyer
(D) teenager

1H Thinking Creatively

Answer each question below. Don't be afraid to think creatively.

1.   Briefly describe the plot of a made-up movie named *The Blasé Butcher*.

_____

2. If you could pick any **tract** of land in the world to build on, what would you choose?

    _____

3. What do you think a **panoramic** camera is?

    _____

4. Why might a government fear **anarchy**?

    _____

5. Explain how a hunter could defend himself from a grizzly bear and **vice versa.**

    _____

Word Breakdown

Panorama comes from the Greek *pan* ("all") and *oramic* ("to see"). A panorama allows you to see all. The prefix "pan" is used in big words like *panacea* (a medicine that cures everything), and also to indicate that all things are included. The airline Pan Am is short for Pan America (they fly all over the Americas). The *Pantheon*, in Rome, is the temple for all the gods. The word *pancake,* however, has nothing to do with "all." Pancake comes from the German word *panne* and the Old Norse word *kaka*.

Blasé has a connotation of: *I've seen the whole world, and now I'm bored.* It is not the boredom of the working man, but the boredom of someone with so much money or time that they don't know what to do. *Blasé* is actually just a French word, and in French slang it means "constantly hung over." An Ella Fitzgerald song, "You're Blasé," contains the lyrics: "You sleep, the sun is shining...There's nothing new for you to do. You're blasé."

Unit 2 - Muhammad Ali

2A Introduction

In the 1960s, a young boxer named Cassius Clay came out of Kentucky, winning lots of fights. He even won the gold medal at the Olympics in Rome when he was only 18 years old. Still, most sports experts didn't think much of Cassius Clay. First, he had the nerve to call himself "the greatest." Second, he had a very strange boxing style, in which he dodged more than he blocked. Third, he would rhyme before a fight – clever freestyles that would later lead people to call him the first rapper ever.

He went on to live up to his self-proclaimed "greatest" title. After switching his name to Muhammad Ali and converting to Islam, the boxer was drafted to fight in the Vietnam War. He refused, arguing that the war was immoral. This got him banned from boxing in the United States for three years, until the Supreme Court decided that Ali should have the right to box. Ali came back in grand style, at an enormous fight, called the Rumble in the Jungle.

2B Song Lyrics

"Float like a butterfly, sting like a bee,
Your hands can't touch what your eyes can't see."

Now everybody's going to say his name: "Ali,"
But he was born Cassius Clay.
From day one, he struggled and **grappled** with the fact
that his grades were bad, he's in the back of the class.
But it was inherited, he had a **heritage**,
To keep his head up and never quit,
This boxer spit more rhymes than Chaucer,
Kept it hotter than water when you're cooking lobster.

"Wooh!" You said it, he had
The appearance or **mien** of a man with a dream.
They say to catch the worm, the birdie's got to get up early,
Well, Ali was faster than the Kentucky Derby.
Oh, he was quick and **agile**,
Fast on his feet, the kid had style,
He won Olympic gold, and came home to eat,
The restaurant said, "Sorry, son, whites only."

Oh, He felt so cold and unsettled
That he went to the river and threw in his gold medal.
This was the time and **era** of the Vietnam War,
And Ali got drafted to fight and serve.
But his **stance** on the war? He thought it was wrong,
"I ain't got no quarrel with them Vietcong."
A man who speaks what he thinks? You said it,
Meditate and **muse** on that for a minute, while I...

Hook

Ali's biggest fight was with George Foreman,
It was **pivotal** in his life, so important.
It went down in Zaire; it was called and **dubbed**
The Rumble in the Jungle.
Foreman was stronger, but Ali was **audacious**,
Fearless and bold, preparing to go round for round.
He had to **muster** and gather the strength
To absorb Foreman's blows.

Nobody knows how Ali had the strength and the **stamina**
To withstand the pain, grab your camera.
'Cause one punch was **exceptional**, it stood out,
And that punch knocked George Foreman down.
The fight was **legendary**, and the story was told
Among the black, the white, and the young and the old.
You could say Ali was on a mission and **crusade**
To prove to the world, "I am the Greatest!"

Hook

2C Words Defined

Below you'll find each vocabulary word that was used in the song. Each word is followed by the part of speech, a simple definition and a meaningful sentence. Some words will also have synonyms, antonyms and other forms of the word listed.

1. agile (adj) able to move quickly and easily; flexible

Cheerleaders are very *agile* as evidenced by their fancy stunts and dance moves.
Synonyms: nimble, spry
Other forms: Chimpanzees have a lot of *agility* (noun) since they are able to swing freely and easily from limb to limb without ever falling to the ground.

2. audacious (adj) bold, daring or uninhibited

The *audacious* young baseball player was eager to work his way up from the minor leagues.
Synonyms: courageous, nervy
Antonyms: timid, cowardly

3. crusade (noun) a military expedition; a campaign for a cause

The king led the *crusade* across the country to take over more land and people.
Other forms: Crusade can also be a verb meaning "to fight for a cause," as in: The sixth graders *crusade* all year long to be able to attend the seventh and eighth grade dances. A *crusader* is one who *crusades*.

4. dub (verb) to choose; to name

The English teacher announced that she was going to *dub* Lawrence the best speller in the entire class.
Synonyms: designate, label

5. era (noun) a period of time marked by distinct events

The invention of the Ford Model T marked a new *era* in travel.

6. exceptional (adj) unusual, extraordinary

Brittney was such an *exceptional* speller that even our English teacher asked her how to spell words.
Synonyms: atypical, phenomenal, peculiar

7. grapple (verb) to struggle with physically or mentally

Steven *grappled* with the idea of losing both his mom and his brother in the car accident.

8. heritage (noun) legacy or tradition

The family had been located in the town for over one hundred years and were very proud of their *heritage*.

9. legendary (adj) well-known or famous

Wild Bill, the outlaw, was *legendary* for his bank robbery hold-ups and gun fights.
Antonyms: obscure, unknown
Other forms: A *legend* (noun) is a story passed down through generations or a person who becomes *legendary*.

10. mien (noun) manner or appearance

The king was a man of honorable *mien*, so the townspeople did not fear him.

11. muse (verb) to think about or ponder something

My dad told me that my problem wasn't that I *mused* to much and that an idle mind was the devil's playground.

12. muster (verb) to gather or to summon

Like many teenage students, Gloria has to *muster* a lot of courage to stand in front of her peers and deliver a speech.
Antonyms: disperse, scatter

13. pivotal (adj) important, vital

A *pivotal* moment in the football game occurred when the opposing team's quarterback fell and broke his arm.
Antonyms: insignificant, minor, incidental
Other forms: A *pivotal* event is like a *pivot* (noun), a pin in the ground around which other things turn.

14. stamina (noun) endurance

Most marathon runners have a lot of *stamina* to run long distances.
Synonyms: staying power, endurance

15. stance (noun) 1. an intellectual or emotional attitude toward something 2. the position of one's feet.

1. Gavin's mom took a negative *stance* on taking drugs because her father had died from a drug addiction. 2. The baseball player's *stance* was awkward, yet he consistently hit home runs when he was at bat.

2D Fix the Mistake

Each of the sentences below has a mistake. The wrong vocabulary words have been used, so the sentences don't make sense. Rewrite each sentence using the correct vocabulary word from this unit.

1. The ballerina was so **audacious** on the stage that she could start and stop her movements on a dime.

    _____

2. It just so happened that during the **exceptional** moment of the play, I had to use the restroom, so I missed most of the plot.

    _____

3. Thomas Jefferson was famous for his unending **mien** to give states more power.

    _____

4. My baseball coach **grappled** me the "home run kid" because I saved every baseball game with a home run.

    _____

5. During the Mesozoic **heritage**, massive dinosaurs roamed parts of the U.S. in Wyoming and Montana

    _____

6. "I think I'm happy because I'm so pretty," the model **mustered.**

    _____

7. The long distance runners had more **stance** than the sprinters.

    _____

8. Barry wanted to break the world record in number of hot dogs eaten in one minute because he wanted to be **agile**, and in people's minds forever.

    _____

9. Even the most **pivotal** stuntman would not attempt to jump between the two buildings.

    _____

10.   Mr. Trump's stern **era** gave away that he was going to fire the employee no matter what she said in her defense.

_____

11.   Rosie's **crusade** was full of famous chefs dating back to the early 1800s.

_____

12.   Mr. Simpson **dubbed** with the idea of whether to take a job as a surgeon or pediatrician.

_____

13.   Susie was shocked when her teacher announced that she had not just done well on the test, but she had done a(n) **legendary** job.

_____

14.   Ozzie had to **muse** the courage to ski down the black diamond slope with his friends.

_____

15.   A strong **stamina** against bullying was taken by the school administration during the school day.

_____

2E Pick the Winner

Circle the word that best fits into the sentence. Then write a sentence below that uses the word you didn't pick in a meaningful way.

1.   Some of our family members were embarrassed by our mob-connected **(stamina OR heritage)**.

2.   _____

3.   When we studied the prehistoric **(era OR crusade)**, I learned that early humans made several advancements in tool making.

4.   _____

5.   Jerry had to **(muster OR dub)** the courage to ask his secret crush, Maryanne, to dance at the prom.

6.   _____

7.   The **(agile OR pivotal)** moment came when Truman decided he wanted to escape.

8.   _____

agile / audacious / crusade / dub / era / exceptional / grapple / heritage / legendary / mien / muse / muster / pivotal / stamina / stance

9.   Some bosses are **(exceptional OR audacious)** at motivating their employees to work more efficiently.

10.   _____

2F Draw the Relationships

In each grouping of eight words below, draw straight lines between the synonyms (words that mean similar things), and draw wiggly lines between any antonyms (words that mean nearly opposite things). Every word should have at least one line connected to it. Some may have more.

1

agile   audacious   crusade   name

battle   nimble   dub   timid

2

era   legacy   grapple   heritage

typical   exceptional   period of time   harmonize

3

legendary   mien   muse   appearance

contemplate   unknown   muster   gather

4

one's personal attitude   stamina   stance   flexible

pivotal   minor   agile   endurance

2G Understanding What You Read

Read the passage below. Then answer the questions.

Despite his <u>audacious</u> claims that he would win the fight, no one gave Muhammad Ali much of a chance to win the big 1974 fight, the Rumble in the Jungle. His opponent, George Foreman, was the current world champion and had beaten two other <u>legendary</u> fighters, both of whom had defeated Ali previously. Foreman was years younger than Ali, and one of the hardest hitters in boxing. Some people were scared that Foreman might accidentally kill Ali in the ring.

Prior to the fight, Ali had boasted about how <u>agile</u> his fighting style was, and that this style would help him defeat Foreman. He had declared that he would run circles around Foreman until he was exhausted and defeated. He had even written a little rap about it: "Now you see me, now you don't. George thinks he will, but I know he won't!" It was with rhymes like that one, not to mention his shining personality, that Ali got many of the fans on his side.

The fight started and seemed to be what everyone predicted: an easy win for Foreman. But Ali, after taking a few punches, didn't give up. Instead he began to employ an <u>exceptional</u> strategy. He took Foreman on early, connecting with several strong right-handed blows, using all the strength and power that he could <u>muster</u>.

For the rest of the fight, Ali simply outlasted Foreman. He would take a <u>stance</u> against the ropes, allowing him to absorb Foreman's punches. It was a strategy that commentators called "the rope-a-dope." In the <u>pivotal</u> eighth round of the fight, Foreman's <u>stamina</u> was gone. Ali was able to knock him out with a quick punch, winning the match.

While the Rumble in the Jungle had become one of the most important sporting events of its <u>era</u>, Ali had become one of the most important sports figures of all time.

1. Before the fight, Ali told the press that he would beat Foreman because he was more
(A) powerful
(B) creative
(C) intelligent
(D) nimble

2. According to the passage, George Foreman
(A) had never actually won a major match before
(B) was the most famous boxer alive
(C) had defeated Ali twice before
(D) was the world champion of boxing

3. According to the text, how was Ali able to gain fans?
(A) punching
(B) rhyming
(C) dancing
(D) matching

4. After getting hit a few times, Ali uses a strategy that is described as
(A) special
(B) a long shot
(C) a sure thing
(D) bizarre

agile / audacious / crusade / dub / era / exceptional / grapple / heritage / legendary / mien / muse / muster / pivotal / stamina / stance

5. What made Ali victorious?
(A) He was a stronger puncher.
(B) He hit Foreman in the head many times.
(C) He let Foreman tire himself out.
(D) He threatened to kill Foreman by accident.

2H Thinking Creatively

Answer each question below. Don't be afraid to think creatively.

1.   If you could be **legendary** for something, what would it be?

_____

2.   Why might the **mien** of an undercover cop be important?

_____

3.   When you get bored in class, what topics do you find yourself **musing** about?

_____

4.   If you were the President, what would be your **stance** on immigration?

_____

5.   Why do you think they call the metal device a **grappling hook**?

_____

Word Breakdown

In Greek mythology, the Muses were goddesses/sprites that inspired people to create art. The nine major Muses were the daughters of Zeus, and each one embodied and inspired a different art form. They were: Calliope (epic poetry), Clio (history), Erato (lyric poetry), Euterpe (music), Melpomene (tragedy), Polyhymnia (religious music), Terpsichore (dance), Thalia (comedy), and Urania (astronomy). There is no official Muse of rap music. Yet.

The Muses were often called upon to help a struggling song writer or author in a time of need. Thus Dante writes, "O Muses! O high genius! Aid me now!" Nowadays, we call anything that is a source of inspiration a muse. It could be your mom, loneliness, love, or an image in your mind. My Muse when I wrote this song was Muhammad Ali himself.

Unit 3 - Wild Ride

3A Introduction

Dreaming is pretty amazing. Each night, we close our eyes and are taken to places where crazy things occur. Sometimes it seems that we can control our dreams and we're able to do whatever we want. Other times, it seems as though our dreams control us, and we're just along for the wild ride.

3B Song Lyrics

Dark clouds filled the afternoon sky,
Another **tedious**, boring day passing by.
I was tired of TV, my laziness was **contagious,**
Spreading, I think I heard a sigh from my neighbor.
But who could have saved us from this boredom?
A board game? I can't stand 'em, I **deplore** them.
I **lolled** on the sofa, lounged with ease,
And like 1, 2, 3, I was counting sheep.

Next thing I knew, my mom was shaking me,
She criticized and **chastised** me for sleeping.
Then a strange thing happened as I opened my eyes,
My mother started to **hover** and float up to the sky.
"Mom! Have you been changed or **modified**?"
I could hardly see, I was borderline blind.
But up she went, through the clouds and toward the stars,
This day got crazy-weird, I mean really **bizarre**...

It's a wild ride...

I found my sister, but she was messed up,
I mean, something with the kid sis was **amiss**.
I asked her, "You okay?" It got wilder yet,
'Cause my sister spoke a real strange **dialect,**
Another language, but not Spanish or Russian,
I mean a crazy tongue from outer space or something.
It might sound ridiculous or **preposterous**,
But she was looking just like a rhinoceros.

Spontaneously, out of the blue,
My mom started to fight me, using kung fu.
Now I don't want to hit my mama so I ran around the corner,
If she hit me with the roundhouse, I would have been a goner.
Nothing could **avail** me or help me out,
So I started to cry and scream and shout.
It all **culminated**, came to an ending though,
When my sister cried, "Dinner time, bro!"

As I opened my eyelids, my dreams **subsided**,
They sunk away like a river's tide did.

But my nightmare wasn't even over yet,
'Cause when I looked at my plate, there was cream of spinach!

Hook

3C Words Defined

Below you'll find each vocabulary word that was used in the song. Each word is followed by the part of speech, a simple definition and a meaningful sentence. Some words will also have synonyms, antonyms and other forms of the word listed.

1. amiss *(adj)* in a faulty way, astray, or wrong

When my parents came home from being gone all weekend, they saw how clean the house was and immediately knew something was *amiss*.
Synonyms: faulty, improper, flawed, askew, awry
Other forms: *Amiss* can also be an adverb: Something's gone *amiss*!

2. avail *(verb)* to be of use to; to help

The doctor's best efforts did not *avail* the dying patient.
Synonyms: to benefit, aid
Other forms: *Avail* can also be a noun meaning "use or advantage" as in: His strength was of little or no *avail* in digging himself out from under the avalanche.

3. bizarre *(adj)* unusual, odd or outrageous

Tracy was exhibiting *bizarre* behavior around James because she had a crush on him.

4. chastise *(verb)* to criticize or discipline

The football coach would *chastise* his players when they were losing.
Synonyms: scold, berate
Antonyms: praise, encourage

5. contagious *(adj)* easily transmittable

Even though Stella's boyfriend had strep throat and was highly *contagious*, she kissed him.

6. culminate *(verb)* to come to the end or the highest point

The flag football tournament will *culminate* with an awards banquet, where I hope to be recognized as the most valuable player.
Synonyms: conclude, finish, peak
Other forms: A huge dinner marked the *culmination* (noun) of the Broadway season.

7. deplore *(verb)* to feel or express strong disapproval of

The group told the President that they *deplored* American involvement in the war.
Synonyms: to bemoan, regret

8. dialect (noun) the language specific to a group of people due to geography, society, or an occupation

Those dudes speak a strange *dialect* of Spanish.

9. hover (verb) to suspend in air; to wait nearby

The cats tend to *hover* by their food dish when they are hungry for breakfast and dinner.
Synonyms: hang, float, linger

10. loll (verb) to lounge; to recline

During summer, the kids like to *loll* about on the dock in their bathing suits beside the lake.
Synonyms: to hang, relax, chill
Antonyms: to hurry, rush, speed

11. modify (verb) to change; to amend

Sometimes my grandmother will *modify* her cookie recipe by adding more sugar so they are sweeter.
Other forms: If you make a *modification* (noun) to something, you make a change to it.

12. preposterous (adj) foolish, absurd

Barry was telling his mom a *preposterous* story about why he was an hour and a half late to school.
Antonyms: reasonable, sensible, logical

13. spontaneous (adj) unplanned and impulsive

There was a *spontaneous* burst of laughter at the back of the classroom when the teacher accidentally said a bad word.

14. subside (verb) to lessen, diminish, decline

The weatherman said the huge waves would *subside* after the hurricane.
Antonyms: to rise, increase

15. tedious (adj) boring, tiring or monotonous

Sharon gave her daughter some *tedious* tasks to complete to pass the time while they waited for their plane to arrive.
Antonyms: entertaining, interesting, exciting

3D Fix the Mistake

Each of the sentences below has a mistake. The wrong vocabulary words have been used, so the sentences don't make sense. Rewrite each sentence using the correct vocabulary word from this unit.

1.   The EMTs did their best to resuscitate the drowning victim, but it was to no **modification**.

_____

2. Since the director of the movie was fascinated by outer space, he included a variety of **contagious**-looking alien creatures in most of the scenes.

    _____

3. Once the flood waters **chastise**, the clean-up efforts will begin.

    _____

4. My high school class reunion weekend will **hover** with a family picnic on Sunday.

    _____

5. She hadn't planned it, but our teacher made a(n) **tedious** decision to act out the day's history lesson instead of read it aloud.

    _____

6. My brother **deplores** about so much that there is a permanent dent in the couch where he sits all day.

    _____

7. While investigating the crime scene, the detective noticed that something was **preposterous** in the bedroom where the murder occurred.

    _____

8. Avital's strong **culmination** made it difficult for us to understand her speech at graduation.

    _____

9. Some teenagers like to **subside** their clothing by cutting and ripping it.

    _____

10. Cinderella didn't mind doing **bizarre** chores around the house because she had her animal friends to cheer her up and keep her company.

    _____

11. My grandmother claims the dog talks to her, but I know that that is **spontaneous**.

    _____

12. The helicopter **lolled** dangerously above the water as the pilot waited for the signal to pull the survivors to safety.

    _____

13. The three-year old was **availed** for drawing on the walls with crayon.

_____

14. Laughter spread room to room like it was **amiss**.

_____

15. Some old people just **loll** young people helping them across the street or down steps because it strips them of their independence.

_____

3E Pick the Winner

Circle the word that best fits into the sentence. Then write a sentence below that uses the word you didn't pick in a meaningful way.

1. Cats are infamous for **(lolling OR hovering)** about all day while dogs are busy running and barking.

2. _____

3. It is **(spontaneous OR preposterous)** to think that one day there will be flying cars and talking robots.

4. _____

5. Marcy wanted to drastically **(subside OR modify)** her bedroom by painting it green and brown like a rainforest and hanging monkeys from the ceiling.

6. _____

7. We called the police to complain about our neighbor's dog, who was incessantly barking, but they could not **(avail OR culminate)** us.

8. _____

9. The patient was so **(contagious OR bizarre)** that he had to be locked in a special wing of the hospital.

10. _____

3F Draw the Relationships

In each grouping of eight words below, draw straight lines between the synonyms (words that mean similar things) and squiggly lines between any antonyms (words that mean nearly opposite things). Every word should have at least one line connected to it. Some may have more.

amiss / avail / bizarre / chastise / contagious / culminate / deplore / dialect / hover / loll / modify / preposterous / spontaneous / subside / tedious

1

avail

punish

chastise

bizarre

benefit

contagious

easily transmittable

normal

2

culminate

deplore

dialect

local speech

wrong

begin

amiss

disapprove of

3

sink

loll

absurd

hover

alter

modify

preposterous

hurry

4

spontaneous

subside

tedious

planned

rise

bizarre

weird

interesting

3G Understanding What You Read

Read the passage below. Then answer the questions.

Ms. Alfonso had said she was ready to quit. During the past year, her <u>bizarre</u> behavior had become more and more erratic and more and more <u>preposterous</u>. She was starting to talk in funny <u>dialects</u> just for everyday things. She told us to turn in our homework with a French accent, and to pack our bags with a Southern drawl.

I had always thought she was a nice teacher, I suppose, and also very interesting. Sure, her lessons were <u>tedious</u> sometimes, going on and on. I wasn't crazy about the way she'd <u>hover</u> over our group in particular whenever she thought something was <u>amiss</u>. You know how they say that a watched pot never boils? Well, I do much better work when I don't feel eyes on me, too!

Still, there were times when she was really nice and funny. She'd <u>modify</u> assignments whenever we were having trouble. She also made <u>spontaneous</u> displays of joy whenever a student who wasn't doing so well turned their work in on time. I always wondered what her home life was like. Was she married? Did she act so strange all the time?

Her weird behavior <u>culminated</u> in an entire class in Latin. That's right, she taught the whole class in Latin. Nobody even speaks Latin. It's a dead language. Suzie begged her to stop because it was giving her a headache, but it was to no <u>avail</u>. Ms. Alfonso merely <u>chastised</u> her in the same foreign tongue. I think we knew then: Ms. Alfonso was ready to go.

1. Overall, how does the narrator seem to feel about Ms. Alfonso?
(A) angry with her
(B) intrigued by her
(C) disgusted by her
(D) proud of her

2. The teacher's "tedious" lessons mean they were
(A) funny
(B) difficult
(C) monotonous
(D) silly

3. The narrator objects to the class being taught in Latin by noting that
(A) the class is bored
(B) she has a headache
(C) Latin is not spoken by anyone
(D) something is amiss with her accent

4. Ms. Alfonso "hovered" over her students because
(A) she thought they were doing something wrong
(B) she wanted to help them
(C) she wanted to teach them a lesson
(D) she wanted to grade their papers

5. The phrase "a watched pot never boils" is used in the passage in order to
(A) indicate how hard it is to boil water
(B) teach the teacher a lesson about what to look at
(C) explain how hard it is to work under the teacher's gaze
(D) show the reader that the narrator isn't boring

3H Thinking Creatively

Answer each question below. Don't be afraid to think creatively.

1. Why do you think certain cultures **deplore** one another?

   _____

2. If you were a rapper, would you rather be named "Tedious" or "Preposterous"? Why?

   _____

3. Describe the story of a book series called *Miss Amiss*.

   _____

4. What is the most **tedious** task you are asked to do by your teachers?

   _____

5.   What's the most **bizarre modification** to a car you've ever heard about?

_____

Word Breakdown

The word *preposterous* means "ridiculous," but breaking it down reveals where that meaning comes from. The word is from the Latin words *pre* and *posterus*. As you probably know, *pre* means "before" (think *prefix*, *pre-game*, *preview*). *Posterus* means "rear or behind" (*posterior* is another word for your buttocks, and a *post-game* report comes after the game). So *preposterous* literally means "before behind." Essentially, it's another way of saying you're mixed up: How could the thing that comes before also be behind? It's like having the cart in front of the horse. In one of his tracks, the rapper Deltron 3030 notes that, "In this modern metropolis, they tries to lock us up under *preposterous* laws."

Unit 4 - We're Coming Up

4A Introduction

Did you know that worldwide, the richest 1% of the population owns 40% of the wealth? Reports show that the gap between the rich and the poor is growing. The rich are getting richer; the poor are getting poorer. Part of this is because money stays in rich nations, such as the United States. But even within the United States, the gap between the rich and the poor is widening.

You probably know the story of Robin Hood: He's a character who decides that the tax on the poor is unfair, so he takes the law into his own hands. He steals from the rich to give to the poor. The Robin Hood of folktales is often considered a hero. But would a Robin Hood today be considered a hero or just another thief?

4B Song Lyrics

It was a dark night and the mood was set,
The waves crashed, the sea was **turbulent**.
The water was wild, but the night was **balmy**,
Soft and mild, nice and lovely.
In the dark my army **groped** our way,
Felt our way to the road, we don't know the way.
We had bread, water and a few other **staples**,
Not those bent metal things, but basic things.

We were **clad** and dressed in black hats and vests,
I looked the best, 'cause my mesh shorts were fresh.
We looked way up at the **citadel**,
The strong castle upon the hill.
It belonged to one R.J. Blake,
While the town starved, he dined on steaks.
While we were working hard to feed our children,
He was throwing fancy parties with Paris Hilton.

This dude was a **tycoon**, I mean, he made
More money off business than Bill Gates.
He had more **revenue** than Mickey D's,
A bigger income stream than the Mississippi.

We're coming up...

I don't want to **vilify** Blake, speak evil of him,
But when the kids on the block see him, they start running.
Some think the rich deserve to be rich,
But to me that's a **fallacy**, a false belief.
'Cause this guy put the "I" in the word the team,
It was up to us to step in and **intervene**.
We moved shadow to shadow up to his mansion,
Then crept through the window, like Robin and Batman.

We collected his jewelry, robbed and **plundered**,
To give to the poor who faced daily hunger.
Carefully, gently and **gingerly**,
We grabbed his silverware, Xbox and TVs.
But then I heard a voice: "You'll **rue** this day!
You'll soon regret it, but never forget it.

"I'm very old, but you can't come in here, yo,
And start eating my cereal, my Cheerios.
This money here? You haven't earned a penny!
You're surrounded by my army of **mercenaries**."
What can I say? They had us arrested, homes,
Now I live in a prison that Blake partially owns.
What do you think? Am I a thug and a thief?
Or a Robin Hood, who just couldn't dodge the police?

Hook

4C Words Defined

Below you'll find each vocabulary word that was used in the song. Each word is followed by the part of speech, a simple definition and a meaningful sentence. Some words will also have synonyms, antonyms and other forms of the word listed.

1. balmy (adj) soothing, refreshing and mild

People change into shorts at the first sign of *balmy* weather.
Synonyms: temperate, tropical, moist
Other forms: A *balm* is a soothing ointment, usually from a plant.

2. citadel (noun) a fortress or stronghold

Only ten warriors remained to defend the *citadel*.

3. clad (verb) dressed, wearing

He was *clad* in a tuxedo.
Other forms: *Clad* is actually considered a past tense form of the verb "to clothe," which is to dress.

4. fallacy (noun) a misleading or false belief

The idea that the world was flat was a popular *fallacy*.

5. gingerly (adverb) cautiously or carefully

The baker *gingerly* placed the decorative flowers on the wedding cake.
Antonyms: carelessly, recklessly
Other forms: *Gingerly* can also be an adjective: He picked up the cat in a *gingerly* way.

6. grope (verb) to search blindly; to feel with your hands

When the lights went out, I *groped* for the switch.
Synonyms: to fumble

7. intervene (verb) to come between; to step in and stop

I had to *intervene* when the two boys fought at the spring dance.
Synonyms: to intrude
Antonyms: to leave alone, withdraw
Other forms: My friends planned an *intervention* (noun) for their best friend, who was addicted to alcohol.

8. mercenary (noun) a professional soldier hired into a foreign army

Pablo is a *mercenary* so he is often away from home for months at a time.

9. plunder (verb) to rob; to pillage

When the pirates sail into port, it is inevitable that they will *plunder* local homes and businesses.
Other forms: *Plunder* can also be a noun meaning "stolen goods or loot," as in: Jack Sparrow's *plunder* consisted of gold and silver coins.

10. revenue (noun) income; earnings

Alison made a lot of *revenue* with her corner lemonade stand during the summer.
Antonyms: expenditure, outgoings, payment

11. rue (verb) to feel sorrow or regret

Tommy will *rue* the day he gets his water gun taken away for good by his mother.
Antonyms: to celebrate, rejoice

12. staple (noun) an important item or raw material

Chocolate was an important *staple* in the Johnson household.
Other forms: Edward hates to *staple* (verb) his papers in class because he has to get up out of his seat to go do it.

13. turbulent (adj) stirred up, disturbed or chaotic

Their marriage was nothing but *turbulent* years of fighting, arguing and unhappiness.
Synonyms: choppy, stormy
Antonyms: settled, calm, manageable
Other forms: There was so much *turbulence* (noun) on the flight that I couldn't read my book or sleep.

14. tycoon (noun) a wealthy and powerful businessperson

Donald Trump is a *tycoon* in New York City and owns lots of real estate.
Synonyms: baron, capitalist, industrialist

15. vilify (verb) to speak evil of; slander

Sandra likes to *vilify* her stepmother with outrageous stories and accusations in order to make her mom smile.
Antonyms: compliment, praise, support

4D Fix the Mistake

Each of the sentences below has a mistake. The wrong vocabulary words have been used, so the sentences don't make sense. Rewrite each sentence using the correct vocabulary word from this unit.

1. The **gingerly** weather was perfect for the swimming and barbecue party.

   _____

2. The only reason the army couldn't overtake the **mercenary** was because it was on a hill.

   _____

3. As a soccer goalie, I was **groped** in long sleeves, pants, knee pads and elbow pads.

   _____

4. When the cats started to fight, I had to **vilify** before they scratched each other to death.

   _____

5. That's the **revenue** of your logic: Just because all dogs are mammals doesn't mean all mammals are dogs.

   _____

6. Kippy would forever **plunder** the day that she drove drunk.

   _____

7. Salt and pepper were **tycoons** that the chef had in her kitchen at all times.

   _____

8. The ocean was so **balmy** that the fishing boat had to call the Coast Guard for a rescue.

   _____

9. When the baby cried in the middle of the night, I **intervened** my way to her cradle in the dark room.

   _____

10.   Betty dreamed of owning an entire company and becoming a real **citadel**.

_____

11.   It was unfortunate that after the hurricane, citizens **clad** all the stores downtown through their broken windows.

_____

12.   Wendy broke a glass in the kitchen and never cleaned it up, so we had to walk **turbulently** around it to avoid cutting our feet.

_____

13.   A **fallacy** lives a tough life: Far from home, he fights a war that he often doesn't care about.

_____

14.   The **staple** from my baseball card business grew tremendously during play-off season.

_____

15.   Candy **rued** her ex-husband in the company of her friends; clearly they had had a messy break-up.

_____

4E Pick the Winner

Circle the word that best fits into the sentence. Then write a sentence below that uses the word you didn't pick in a meaningful way.

1.   The **(tycoon OR mercenary)** owned four of the top five toy manufacturing companies in the U.S.

2.   _____

3.   Cheerios is a **(citadel OR staple)** of every household that has small children.

4.   _____

5.   All of the **(revenue OR fallacy)** from the middle school dance went to pay for the end-of-the-year field trip.

6.   _____

7.   Surfers make sure the ocean is not too **(turbulent OR balmy)** before they paddle out to the breaking sets.

8.   _____

balmy / citadel / clad / fallacy / gingerly / grope / intervene / mercenary / plunder / revenue / rue / staple / turbulent / tycoon / vilify]

9.   To show their team spirit, the crowd all came to the game **(clad OR rue)** in blue hats, shirts and pants.

10.   _____

4F Draw the Relationships

In each grouping of eight words below, draw straight lines between the synonyms (words that mean similar things) and squiggly lines between any antonyms (words that mean nearly opposite things). Every word should have at least one line connected to it. Some may have more.

1

                naked   tropical

castle   fallacy

balmy   truth

                citadel   clad

2

                grope   intervene

gingerly   fumble

professional soldier   step in

              carelessly   mercenary

3

                enjoy   unimportant item

plunder   staple

revenue   earnings

              steal   rue

4

                baron   criticize

turbulent   fallacy

tycoon   settled

              lie   vilify

4G Understanding What You Read

Read the passage below. Then answer the questions.

Captain Julie Mays crawled up the hill on her knees. <u>Clad</u> in her army fatigues, she <u>groped</u> her way through the mud, keeping her head down. The gunfire overhead was getting louder and louder. Julie hated this. She knew she would rather be at home, playing with her brand-new puppy, lying in her bed or making grilled cheese sandwiches.

She shook the thoughts out of her head. She was a <u>mercenary</u> now. It was her job to be a soldier - that's what she was being paid for and that's what she would do. And despite the turbulence of her emotions, she was out here in the field. This was war, and there weren't going to be any grilled cheese sandwiches.

She started to rue the day she had taken the assignment. She had done plenty of dangerous missions, but something was wrong with this one. She thought of the mysterious tycoon who was paying her. He had asked her to break in to this citadel and plunder whatever she could find.

As the explosions got louder, Julie rolled over. She didn't like this assignment anymore. It was getting far too dangerous in this jungle to care about the money she was making. She gingerly climbed forward and peered around the boulder she was hiding behind.

Her enemy stood there with her hand on her hips. Julie's skills at hiding had saved her before, and perhaps they would save her from trouble now. "Julie Mays!" the voice, deep and booming, yelled out. "Come out now!"

Julie knew it was now or never. She had to make a break for it. She gathered her courage and ran. She hadn't gotten far when the tall woman grabbed her arm. But then the woman reached down and kissed the top of her head. Julie looked up at her, not knowing what to expect.

"Come on honey. We're going home now." Julie held her mom's hand, and they walked out of the furniture store together.

1. In the text, the main character, Julie, is
(A) dying
(B) escaping
(C) pretending
(D) crying

2. The word "turbulence" is used in the second paragraph to indicate
(A) choppy waves
(B) jittery nervousness
(C) total insanity
(D) rough wind

3. "She started to rue the day she had taken the assignment" means she
(A) worshipped the day
(B) planned the day
(C) mourned the day
(D) remember the day

4. In Julie's own mind, she is
(A) an awkward mercenary
(B) a boring shopping partner
(C) a perfect daughter
(D) a soldier now

5. The narrator of the story
(A) misleads the reader into thinking something that isn't true
(B) stays honest throughout the tale
(C) describes every detail of the store
(D) thinks that Julie should stop what she's doing

balmy / citadel / clad / fallacy / gingerly / grope / intervene / mercenary / plunder / revenue / rue / staple / turbulent / tycoon / vilify]

4H Thinking Creatively

Answer each question below. Don't be afraid to think creatively.

1.   Is it ever OK to **plunder** for **staples**? If so, when?

   _____

2.   If there was an intruder in your house and you had to **grope** for a weapon at night to defend yourself, what would you use?

   _____

3.   What things might a friend do that would prompt you to **intervene** in order to save them**?**

   _____

4.   Give one example of a commonly believed **fallacy**.

   _____

5.   What things might you say or do when you are **vilifying** someone you dislike?

   _____

Word Breakdown

The word *mercenary* actually has the same root as the word *market*. They both come from the old Italian root *merk,* which means "related to sales." So a mercenary sells himself, and a market (or *mercado* in Spanish) sells goods.

The *fy* on the end of *vilify* means "to make." You see this in lots of words: *pacify* ("make peaceful"), *codify* ("make into a code"), *dignify* ("make special"), specify ("make specific"). Some people like to play with this ending to create new words, usually as a joke. So next time you trick your friend, you can say, "You've been punked," or you can say, "You've been *punkified*."

Unit 5 - It's Alright

5A Introduction

It is always difficult to realize a dream – to make a dream come true. But it is especially difficult when you are the first person to achieve your dream. Jackie Robinson, the first African-American to play major league baseball, was booed and heckled when he took the field. Because Galileo argued that the sun, not the Earth, was at the center of the solar system, the Catholic Church had him arrested. This is the story of Nydia Velázquez, the first Puerto Rican woman elected to Congress.

5B Song Lyrics

I was born in a small Puerto Rican town
Of no fame, and little **renown**.
House wasn't **capacious**, it was small,
About nine kids bouncing off the walls.
I **attribute** my spirit to my father,
He's the cause of it, working hard but
He never acted **servile**, he never said,
"Yes sir, whatever you say sir, right away."

Sometimes he launched into a **tirade**,
An angry speech against the way
Workers cutting down sugarcane
Were treated: It wasn't kind or **humane**.
They'd get hurt, but they didn't have
Access or **recourse** to the courts.
My dad said never **forfeit**, never give up,
And if they swing at you, throw your hands up.

It's alright. It's alright. It's alright.

Well, I grew up and flew up, up to New York,
And I moved up like rulers, up to the top.
The **ultimate**, greatest possible feat:
I ran for Congress, and won a seat.
Does that seem **plausible**, believable?
I'm a congresswoman, yes it's really true.
I'm **liberal**, I want things to change,
Conservative means you want things to stay the same.

I've **advocated** for raising pay,
I pleaded cases to increase the **wage**.
Plus I **waged** war against the guns,
'Cause guns in the streets make the blood run.
I want to **inaugurate** and begin,
A new policy for immigrants.
My lesson: Don't let people stop you,
And if you live in New York, I represent for you.

Hook

advocate / attribute / capacious / conservative / forfeit / humane / inaugurate / liberal / plausible / recourse / renown / servile / tirade / ultimate / wage

5C Words Defined

Below you'll find each vocabulary word that was used in the song. Each word is followed by the part of speech, a simple definition and a meaningful sentence. Some words will also have synonyms, antonyms and other forms of the word listed.

1. advocate (verb) to argue for, recommend or urge

Our student council representative is going to *advocate* for a longer lunch period on Fridays.
Other forms: My neighbor is a strong *advocate* (noun) of saving the rainforests.

2. attribute (verb) to consider as caused by something else

The firefighters *attributed* the forest fire to arson.
Other forms: *Attribute* can also be a noun meaning "a quality or characteristic," as in: Honesty is an *attribute* that many people look for in politicians.

3. capacious (adj) spacious, roomy

The Physical Education department needed a *capacious* bin in which to store all of the sporting equipment.
Synonyms: voluminous, ample, commodious

4. conservative (adj) favoring traditional views; against change

She is such a *conservative* dresser; she only wears full-length skirts and dresses.
Other forms: A *conservative* person (or especially someone who votes that way) is considered a *conservative* (noun).

5. forfeit (verb) to give up or surrender

My grandmother had to *forfeit* her purse to the mugger to avoid being pushed down and beaten up.
Synonyms: to give over, relinquish

6. humane (adj) marked by compassion or tenderness for humans or animals

People are not very *humane* to their pets if they leave them locked in a hot car while they dine or shop.
Synonyms: caring, compassionate, altruistic
Antonyms: cruel, mean, malicious

7. inaugurate (verb) 1. to begin 2. to officially bring into office

The end of the war will hopefully *inaugurate* a time of peace between the two countries. 2. The ninth President of the United States was *inaugurated* in March and was dead by April.
Synonyms: commence, initiate
Other forms: The *inaugural* (adj) ball took place after the *inauguration* (noun).

8. liberal (adj) 1. favoring progress and reform over tradition 2. generous

One of the most *liberal* people in Omaha, Karl wanted everyone to have healthcare.
Other forms: *Liberal* is also a noun meaning "a person who advocates open-mindedness and liberal views," as in: The politician labeled himself a *liberal*.

9. plausible (adj) believable

Some of the first graders' stories did not have *plausible* plots, but they were still very cute to read.
Antonyms: unlikely, implausible, doubtful

10. recourse (noun) the option of having someone or something for help

Chaz felt he had no *recourse*; he had to take matters into his own hands.
Synonym: alternative

11. renown (noun) widespread fame

The audience was in awe of the celebrity's *renown* when he entered the room.
Antonyms: anonymity, obscurity, oblivion
Other forms: If you are famous, you are *renowned* (adj).

12. servile (adj) groveling or extremely submissive

The new recruits expressed *servile* obedience to their superiors.

13. tirade (noun) a long, violent speech

My dad went on a *tirade* about my messy room and yelled my ear off.
Synonyms: outburst, rant, diatribe

14. ultimate (adj) last, final or greatest

It was Serena's *ultimate* goal in life to get straight A's on all of her essays.
Synonyms: final, paramount, greatest

15. wage (verb) to carry on a battle or conflict

The students wanted to *wage* a war against hunger in their community and have a yearlong food drive.
Other forms: *Wage* is also a noun meaning "payment for labor or services," as in: As a busboy, I did not earn a very high *wage*.

5D Fix the Mistake

Each of the sentences below has a mistake. The wrong vocabulary words have been used, so the sentences don't make sense. Rewrite each sentence using the correct vocabulary word from this unit.

1.   Martha Stewart **advocates** her success to hard work and wise money management.

   _____

2.   The photography club is going to **forfeit** me as their president next week at the first meeting of the year.

   _____

advocate / attribute / capacious / conservative / forfeit / humane / inaugurate / liberal / plausible / recourse / renown / servile / tirade / ultimate / wage

3. Since it wasn't **conservative** for Stanley to clean the entire garage by himself, my brother and I decided to help him.

    _____

4. As a fast food worker, my **tirades** were not enough for me to move out of my parents' house.

    _____

5. The locker room was not **liberal** enough for the entire football team and their equipment.

    _____

6. Sarah was such a(n) **renowned** cat owner that all ninety-eight cats had their own food and water dish.

    _____

7. After seeing how Tim bossed Pam around, I definitely knew that she acted **ultimate** to him in their relationship.

    _____

8. His only **wage** was to go to the police.

    _____

9. The eighth graders are **inaugurating** for a graduation dance that lasts all night.

    _____

10. Our coach completely lost his temper whenever we had to **attribute** a soccer game due to limited players.

    _____

11. I don't know if he's going to dress up like a woman for the play; he's pretty **capacious**.

    _____

12. Jane was **humane** with her ice cream servings, so everyone had more than enough.

    _____

13. Hercules was **servile** for his size and strength.

    _____

14. No one ever cheated in Mr. Tong's class because they would have to endure one of his horrendous **recourses.**

    _____

15.   **Plausibly**, I'd like to end up living in a foreign country, but it might not happen for a while.

_____

5E Pick the Winner

Circle the word that best fits into the sentence. Then write a sentence below that uses the word you didn't pick in a meaningful way.

1.   Slaves had to be **(servile OR liberal)** to their masters or suffer the consequences.

2.   _____

3.   In our school, Lilly has more **(tirades OR renown)** than even the star athletes, because of her amazing mohawk.

4.   _____

5.   Painting houses for a living, I was paid a good **(recourse OR wage)**.

6.   _____

7.   Clara **(attributed OR forfeited)** her intelligence to her parents, who were both famous inventors.

8.   _____

9.   The more **(conservative OR capacious)** the house was, the more likely the Brady Bunch could fit in it.

10.   _____

5F Draw the Relationships

In each grouping of eight words below, draw straight lines between the synonyms (words that mean similar things) and squiggly lines between any antonyms (words that mean nearly opposite things). Every word should have at least one line connected to it. Some may have more.

1

a quality   wage

attribute   promote

advocate   final

fight   ultimate

advocate / attribute / capacious / conservative / forfeit / humane / inaugurate / liberal / plausible / recourse / renown / servile / tirade / ultimate / wage

2

roomy   forfeit

surrender   liberal

capacious   mean

conservative   humane

....

3

celebrity   servile

inaugurate   begin

tirade   whisper

bossy   renown

....

4

plausible   recourse

progressive   conservative

unbelievable   alternative

traditional   liberal

5G Understanding What You Read

Read the passage below. Then answer the questions.

It was the <u>ultimate</u> insult to Nydia Velázquez. Someone had released her medical records to the opposing campaign, and they had used the sensitive information against her in the 1992 race for the House of Representatives. It was neither a kind nor <u>humane</u> way to run a campaign, but it was a reality nevertheless.

Her opponent had suggested that among her <u>attributes</u> were both mental instability and depression. The newspaper reported that, according to her medical records, she had once attempted suicide. Obviously, it was a way to suggest that Velázquez was not fit to hold office. The goal was obviously to get her to <u>forfeit</u> her campaign. However, Velázquez knew that if she quit at this point, she would never forgive herself. From her childhood, she had dreamed of one day being in a position to help out others around her. She decided not to drop out of the race.

Instead, Velázquez quickly called a press conference. She decided to fight her opponents' charges head on. She didn't deny anything. She told the reporters that yes, she had suffered from depression, but so had millions of other Americans. In fact, 15% of Americans battle major depression at some point in their lives. Velázquez reported that she had undergone counseling, and that her mental health was now very good. She said she was saddened by the tactics her <u>conservative</u> opponents were using in order to win the race, but that she wouldn't stoop to their level. She also went on to say what she would do as a Representative - that she would continue to <u>advocate</u> for better <u>wages</u> and a better way of life for the people of New York City.

Nydia Velázquez beat her opponents in the race for Representative, and became the first Puerto Rican woman to serve in Congress. Since then, she has gone on to a career of great <u>renown</u> as a ranking member of Congress.

1. What could be considered the main theme of the passage?
(A) depression
(B) overcoming difficulties
(C) winning
(D) being Puerto Rican

2. According to the text, the main strategy of Velázquez's opponents was to argue that
(A) Velasquez lacked experience, since she had never held office before
(B) a Latin woman isn't fit for office
(C) Velasquez shouldn't hold office because of her problems with depression
(D) she was too liberal to represent New Yorkers

3. To "advocate for better wages" means to
(A) talk about better conditions
(B) help employees join unions
(C) argue for higher pay
(D) strike for improved managers

4. Why did Velázquez note that 15% of Americans will suffer from major depression at some point in their lives?
(A) to show that America has a major health care issue that must be addressed
(B) to encourage depressed individuals to seek help
(C) to show that she was strong and would fight her mental illness
(D) to demonstrate that she was not alone and shouldn't be considered an outcast

5. Nydia Velázquez is employed by
(A) a school district
(B) the government
(C) the press
(D) a hospital

5H Thinking Creatively

Answer each question below. Don't be afraid to think creatively.

1. What would it mean if you **advocated** for **conservatives**?

    _____

2. Explain how zoos could be more **humane.**

    _____

3. If you could design the ceremony, how would you **inaugurate** the next president of the United States?

    _____

advocate / attribute / capacious / conservative / forfeit / humane / inaugurate / liberal / plausible / recourse / renown / servile / tirade / ultimate / wage

4.   As a student, what the least **plausible** excuse you have ever heard for a peer not doing their homework?

_____

5.   What might a shop called *Tirades 'R' Us* sell?

_____

Word Breakdown

The word *conservative* is derived from "someone who likes to conserve." To *conserve* is to protect or use sparingly. You can help conserve the environment by conserving energy and turning off your lights when you leave the house. *Conserve* comes from the Latin *com*, which is an intensifier, and *servare*, which means "to maintain or keep." Someone who is conservative wants to conserve tradition. It's often liberals, however, who are more interested in conserving the environment.

Liberal has the same root as *liberty* and so is related to freedom. A liberal person was free in how they spoke or acted, not bound by tradition. It was originally used as an insult, but took on a positive connotation later on. Nowadays it can be used in ways that are both positive and negative. Today, in American politics, Democrats are more liberal, while Republicans are more conservative, though that wasn't always the case.

Unit 6 - How to Be an Entrepreneur

6A Introduction

An entrepreneur is someone who starts his or her own business. Obviously, it's a lot easier to go work for someone else, and it's a lot less risky. But every entrepreneur knows that if you can successfully make your business grow, then you get to live your dream. It's like Jay-Z says: "I'm not a businessman. I'm a business, *man*!"

We started Flocabulary with nothing but a dream and a couple thousand dollars. Whenever we're on TV or the radio, people ask us what advice we have for young entrepreneurs. Well, consider this our answer.

6B Song Lyrics

Step one: Learn to **discern** between
A good idea and a hair-brained scheme.
Be **inventive**, create new things,
'Cause new inventions will get you paid real big.

Two: Keep your enemies next to you,
In your **perspective** and your view.
You better **rebuke** and criticize those foes
Who want to step. "Where?" All up on your toes.

Three: Don't get greedy like monopoly,
It could turn evil like an **atrocity**.
And don't work from time to time, **sporadically**,
That plan's got holes like a cavity.

Four: Be a **voracious** reader, read more books,
No weirdo stuff, you'll get zero bucks.

Five: Be a strong leader to **exemplify**,
And show your people how to live their lives.
Your enemies are the competition, so listen:
Deploy your troops, get 'em in position.

Six: You can eat Chex Mix, but don't mix checks, dude,
Get someone to support and **abet** you.
When you do math, be **fastidious**,
Pay mad attention to math equations.

Seven: Can't do it? "Nope." Not **feasible**?
You can't fly to the moon in a station wagon.
If you can't hear the TV you need some **captions**,
Those words below, take it from your captain.

Step eight: You must **evolve** and change,
Like a chimpanzee to a human being.

Step nine: I make rhymes, but I **minimize** the times it takes,
Keep it small like a model's waist.

Ten: Stack paper, but give some back
To those who have less, they can live on that.
Greed can be stinky like manure,
This is how to be an entrepreneur...

6C Words Defined

Below you'll find each vocabulary word that was used in the song. Each word is followed by the part of speech, a simple definition and a meaningful sentence. Some words will also have synonyms, antonyms and other forms of the word listed.

1. abet (verb) to assist, encourage or support, usually in some wrongdoing

George will *abet* Louie in the bank robbery by driving the getaway car.
Other forms: An *abettor*, or *abetter* (noun) assists another in some sort of wrongdoing.

2. atrocity (noun) an appalling condition; the act of being shockingly cruel or inhumane

The biggest *atrocity* of the war was the horrible treatment of women and children in the prison camps.
Other forms: Sadly, the kids at the orphanage were sleeping in *atrocious* (adj) beds of filth, lice and stains.

3. caption (noun) an explanation or description for a picture

Daphne did not read the *caption* under the cartoon, so she did not get its meaning.
Other forms: *Caption* can also be a verb meaning "to entitle something," as in: The yearbook editor asked us to *caption* each and every photograph.

4. discern (verb) to detect or perceive as separate and distinct

The students were able to *discern* that their teacher was not happy with them after she read the notes left by her substitute.
Synonyms: distinguish, differentiate
Antonyms: disregard, overlook

5. deploy (verb) to spread out or move into a position of readiness

If the landing gear doesn't *deploy* on time, the plane will crash on the runway.
Other forms: The large *deployment* (noun) of troops to Iraq meant that the war was not over yet.

6. evolve (verb) to develop over time or gradually

Over the next two weeks, the seeds we planted in science class will *evolve* into different types of plants.
Synonyms: emerge, grow, metamorphose
Other forms: A popular video on the Internet features a man showing the *evolution* (noun) of dance.

7. exemplify (verb) to show by example, or to be an example of

Our student body president tries to *exemplify* the characteristics of a good leader and friend.
Synonyms: demonstrate, display

8. fastidious (adj) demanding, painstaking or hard to please

Bruno is a *fastidious* cleaner because he sweeps, mops and vacuums his entire house daily.
Synonyms: careful, meticulous, discriminating

9. feasible (adj) capable of being accomplished; possible

My plan to steal a car was *feasible*, but I was too lazy to carry it out.
Antonyms: impossible, unlikely

10. inventive (adj) creative

Valerie was an *inventive* fashion designer and often won awards for her unique clothing designs.
Synonyms: artistic, innovative
Other forms: As you probably know, an *inventor* (noun) *invents* (verb) *inventions* (noun).

11. minimize (verb) to reduce to the smallest amount

Lyndsay's doctor tried to *minimize* the amount of pain she felt following her knee surgery.
Synonyms: downplay, diminish, lessen
Antonyms: enhance, exaggerate, maximize
Other forms: The smallest amount is the *minimum* (noun).

12. perspective (noun) a view, or a mental view or outlook

From my *perspective* at the back of the classroom, it looked as if Kayeesha was cheating off of Joey's test.

13. rebuke (verb) to criticize sharply or disapprove of

A teacher most likely will *rebuke* a student for chewing gum in class.
Synonyms: berate, admonish, reprimand
Other forms: *Rebuke* is also a noun meaning "a criticism or admonishment" as in: The police officer gave the teenager a sharp *rebuke* for speeding in a residential area.

14. sporadic (adj) not happening often; occasional

Mary experiences *sporadic* moments of happy memories of her late husband.

Synonyms: scattered, spotty, infrequent
Antonyms: steady, continuous, frequent
Other forms: The bride *sporadically* (adverb) placed rose petals up and down the aisle of the church.

15. voracious (adj) marked by a large appetite for food or an activity

Timothy was such a *voracious* reader that the librarian let him check out more than the allowable number of books.
Synonyms: avid, unquenchable, insatiable
Antonyms: quenched, satisfied, indifferent

6D Fix the Mistake

Each of the sentences below has a mistake. The wrong vocabulary words have been used, so the sentences don't make sense. Rewrite each sentence using the correct vocabulary word from this unit.

1. The outlaw hired me to **deploy** him in the train robbery.

     _____

2. We knew it had been a bad situation for a long time, but we stepped in when it became a(n) **caption.**

     _____

3. Jenna's mom **discerned** her for talking back to her in front of their friends.

     _____

4. Early humans **exemplified** over time from simple creatures to toolmakers.

     _____

5. For a toddler, Daniel was a truly **fastidious** eater, often eating more than his father.

     _____

6. In the winter, it's just not **inventive** to wear shorts in Boston, no matter how much I want to.

     _____

7. Since it was foggy, we only saw **perspective** bursts of fireworks in the night sky.

     _____

8. Grandma tried to **evolve** the amount of damage she did to the car as she relayed the story of her accident to Grandpa.

     _____

9.   The **atrocity** under the political cartoon was another jab at the President's job approval rating.

      _____

10.   The police **abetted** ten different search parties into the forest to cover the most area and hopefully find the lost little girl before darkness fell.

      _____

11.   All kindergarten teachers should **minimize** good behavior because their students are so impressionable.

      _____

12.   No matter how hard I try, I can never please my **sporadic** boss.

      _____

13.   It was difficult to **rebuke** whether my mom was crying out of happiness or sadness.

      _____

14.   Brian was so **voracious** with his toy blocks that he built an entire city on the living room floor.

      _____

15.   From my **feasible**, it was very clear: We needed a bigger boat.

      _____

6E Pick the Winner

Circle the word that best fits into the sentence. Then write a sentence below that uses the word you didn't pick in a meaningful way.

1.   In history, we had to read a lot about the **(atrocities OR perspectives)** of World War II.

2.   _____

3.   Our teacher tried to **(discern OR minimize)** our talking in the library while the librarian read aloud to us.

4.   _____

5.   All of my dates are afraid to return me home past my curfew out of fear of being **(abetted OR rebuked)** by my father.

6.   _____

7.   Despite what the brochure said, Ginger didn't think it was **(feasible OR fastidious)** for her to lose over a hundred pounds in only six months.

8.   _____

9.   Once Maya came out of her coma, she only had **(sporadic OR inventive)** memories of her life before the accident.

10. _____

6F Draw the Relationships

In each grouping of eight words below, draw straight lines between the synonyms (words that mean similar things) and squiggly lines between any antonyms (words that mean nearly opposite things). Every word should have at least one line connected to it. Some may have more.

1

abet   send out   deploy

explanation

horrible   assist

atrocious   caption

2

demanding   demonstrate

discern   evolve

adapt   overlook

exemplify   fastidious

3

inventive   increase

impossible   perspective

feasible   creative

viewpoint   minimize

4

outlook   voracious

rebuke   perspective

sporadic   compliment

frequent   hungry

49

6G Understanding What You Read

Read the passage below. Then answer the questions.

Kelli finished explaining the <u>inventive</u> plan to her dad in detail and waited for his response.

"That's not entirely <u>feasible</u>," he said, sharply. "You need to be more <u>fastidious</u> when it comes to planning. I don't think you've accounted for every alternative. Have you really thought about every detail? What if your mother comes home early?"

Kelli wasn't prepared for this sharp <u>rebuke</u>. She had expected excitement from her father, not a lecture. "But Dad, look at it from my <u>perspective</u>. It's going to be extremely fun, and Mom is going to love it. She wouldn't suspect a thing." Kelli put on her sad face and hoped the expression would get her dad to appreciate her plan, maybe even get him to <u>abet</u> in the planning.

Slowly, she saw her dad's eyes change direction. She watched the expression on his face <u>evolve</u> from disbelief to a small smile. "Well, I suppose that if we were to <u>minimize</u> the amount we talked about it, and if we planned it together, maybe it could work."

Man, Kelli thought, any time she <u>deployed</u> her "sad face," she could get her dad to agree to whatever she wanted. Kelli smiled at the thought, and wondered how old she'd be before that stopped working.

1. The passage suggests that the daughter is trying to be
(A) funny
(B) sneaky
(C) mean
(D) feasible

2. According to the text, the dad seems easily
(A) persuaded by his daughter
(B) saddened by his daughter
(C) angered by his daughter
(D) amused by his daughter

3. Most likely, Kelli is planning to
(A) convince her mother to get back together with her father
(B) get her mother taken to an insane asylum
(C) throw a surprise party for her mother
(D) do the laundry for her mother

4. Kelli's father criticizes her plan by noting that she should be more
(A) inventive
(B) fastidious
(C) voracious
(D) feasible

5. After Kelli puts on her "sad face," her father's reaction is to
(A) immediately agree to her plan
(B) consider her plan more seriously
(C) tell her it's not possible
(D) tell her to stay tight-lipped

6H Thinking Creatively

Answer each question below. Don't be afraid to think creatively.

1.   If you had to give your life a one-lined **caption**, what would it be?

    _____

2.   What is the best **perspective** from which to watch a baseball game?

    _____

3.   In what ways will the human race **evolve** in the next thousand years?

    _____

4.   Name and explain the one athlete or celebrity that you think small children should not **exemplify**.

    _____

5.   How might a **voracious**, yet **sporadic** person behave?

    _____

Word Breakdown

Though the words don't seem similar *caption* is actually related to *capture*. They both stem from the Latin *capere*, meaning "to take." To *capture* is to take something. Originally, when a government seized or captured your property for some reason, it would hand you a "Certificate of Caption," to let you know why they had to repossess it. By 1789, *caption* was being used to mean a chapter heading or title of an article. A hundred years later, it had become "a description of an illustration or photograph."

If you are deaf or watching TV in a restaurant with the sound off, you might want to turn on the "closed captions," which display the text of what is being said on the TV. They are "closed" in that not all viewers see them, only those who turn the captions on. In Nas' song "Nature Shines," he notes that, "For those asking, I flow for TV, HBO and closed captions."

Unit 7 - Ray's Way

7A Introduction

Ray Charles was one of the most influential rhythm and blues musicians in the world. His voice was both smooth and rough, an unmistakable blend. His piano playing was simple but swinging. And the way he'd rock back and forth behind his piano, smiling and howling, is an image no one who saw him can forget.

Born in 1930, in Florida, Ray didn't become blind until he was six years old, when a disease robbed him of his sight. Always a musician, Ray left home at 17 to seek his fame and fortune. Things were hard for many years, but Ray's unique blend of gospel, rhythm and blues, and country soon won him a large audience. Perhaps more than his music, it was the passion that Ray brought to it that we will remember him by. For him, that was just his way.

7B Song Lyrics

Ray was born poor in Florida,
In a shack about the size of a **corridor**.
This was 1930, the month of September,
You can read more about it in his **memoir**.

Ray's mother could barely even pay the bills,
But she **fostered**, encouraged his musical skills.
These were lessons that were **instilled** in him,
Given again and again till they're sinking in.
Blindness was a **shackle** like a handcuff,
That he wore all the time, and times were tough.
Ray wasn't **conventional**, never ordinary,
He added backup singers, the more the merry

Er, some said, "Be the same as us, **assimilate**,"
But the way Ray plays is Ray's way.
So, if you stand in Ray's way, you better make way,
You should have seen him on his pay day.
They **allotted** the pay, and divided it up,
But Ray demanded that they pay him in ones.
In case the manager tried to get **deceptive**,
And trick Ray, in case Ray got less than the rest did.

Say, "Ohhh!"
Say, "Yeah, yeah!"
Say, "Hey!"
That's Ray's way.

The main subject and **theme** of his life,
Was to be the brightest light you're seeing at night.
Music was the **haven** where Ray escaped,
He sang a little melody, and piano-played.
Nothing fancy or flashy, nothing **ornate**,

Just a lil' R&B in a Gospel way.
It sounded **sublime** like summertime,
High and amazing the lines would climb,

And **surpass** the song that was sung before,
Went beyond them; man, it's off the wall.
Ray supplied the notes like a **bountiful** feast,
With so much food that you're dying to eat.
It's an interesting occurrence, a **phenomenon**,
That lots of musical greats are totally blind:
Stevie Wonder, Art Tatum, Blind Lemon Jefferson,
And Ray could pound the keys with the best of them.

Hook

7C Words Defined

Below you'll find each vocabulary word that was used in the song. Each word is followed by the part of speech, a simple definition and a meaningful sentence. Some words will also have synonyms, antonyms and other forms of the word listed.

1. allot (verb) to distribute or divide into portions or shares

On Halloween, I always *allot* each trick-or-treater the same amount of candy no matter how scary their costumes are in comparison to each other.
Synonyms: to pass out, allocate
Antonyms: to keep, retain, withhold

2. assimilate (verb) to incorporate or absorb something; to adjust to

Hot dogs, though originally German, became so *assimilated* into American culture that they now seem truly American.
Other forms: Ping's *assimilation* (noun) into American culture was quick and easy.

3. bountiful (adj) having a lot; plentiful

Our math teacher had a *bountiful* supply of sharpened number two pencils in her desk drawer.
Synonyms: big, ample, copious

4. conventional (adj) standard; ordinary

My parents chose to drive the more *conventional* way home as opposed to the scenic route.
Synonyms: common, traditional
Other forms: A *convention* (noun) is both a normal practice (like shaking hands when you meet someone) and a big gathering of people (like the Whale Watchers Convention).

5. deceptive (adj) misleading or dishonest

It wasn't until my ninth birthday that I realized my parents had been *deceptive* about the existence of the tooth fairy.
Other forms: A *deception* (noun) is a lie.

6. foster (verb) to encourage or care for

Ms. C tried to *foster* creativity in all her students.
Synonyms: promote, cultivate, support
Antonyms: neglect, suppress

7. haven (noun) a refuge or safe place

My mom always says that the health spa is her true *haven*.
Synonyms: retreat, sanctuary, asylum

8. instill (verb) to introduce gradually; implant

It is important to *instill* good manners into children when they are young.
Synonyms: implant, infuse

9. memoir (noun) a written account of one's personal life

Bill Clinton's memoir, *My Life*, was a best seller for many months.
Synonyms: biography, anecdote

10. ornate (adj) decorated in a very fancy, flashy style

I was envious of Sydney's jewelry box because it was filled with *ornate* necklaces, earrings and bracelets.
Synonyms: glitzy, gaudy
Antonyms: plain, unadorned, austere
Other forms: *Ornate* is related to *ornament* (noun), a decoration you might put on your Christmas tree.

11. phenomenon (noun) an observable event; something that is extraordinary

Again and again in nature we see an interesting phenomenon: Storms in the Gulf of Mexico become powerful hurricanes.
Other forms: The celebrity looked *phenomenal* (adj), really extraordinary, after her makeover.

12. shackle (noun) a device (usually metal) that restricts the movement of a prisoner, like handcuffs

Our abductors threatened to tighten our *shackles* unless we stopped screaming for help.
Other forms: *Shackle* is also a verb meaning "to confine or restrain," as in: The kidnappers *shackled* the reporter to a pipe in their backyard.

13. sublime (adj) supreme, outstanding or lofty

There is a *sublime* view from the peak of any mountain.
Synonyms: divine, heavenly
Antonyms: lowly, gross, unattractive

14. surpass (verb) to exceed or go beyond

The Olympic athlete tried to *surpass* the world record time in his first race.
Antonyms: to lose, retreat, fall behind

15. theme (noun) 1. the main subject or unifying idea 2. the music associated with a TV show or person (short for theme song)

1. The *theme* of the story "To Build a Fire" is survival. 2. The Batman *theme* is one of the most famous songs, even though there is only one word in it: *Batman!*

7D Fix the Mistake

Each of the sentences below has a mistake. The wrong vocabulary words have been used, so the sentences don't make sense. Rewrite each sentence using the correct vocabulary word from this unit.

1. During standardized testing, students are **shackled** two pencils and five pieces of scratch paper.

    _____

2. The injured wild chimpanzee had to **foster** to its new home at the animal rescue sanctuary, which took three months.

    _____

3. Our P.E. teacher always tried to **surpass** teamwork in us as she taught different sports and

    games all year long.

    _____

4. The movie's main **memoir** was about the importance of friendship.

    _____

5. The party was **bountiful**, an amazing mix of good people, great music, and delicious food.

    _____

6. Her ability to predict car accidents was a strange **haven**.

    _____

7. It was **conventional** of our teacher to tell us that the test would be all multiple choice and then change it to an essay test.

    _____

8. The reception hall was so **sublimely** decorated; it looked like someone had thrown shiny jewels over everything.

    _____

9. I decided to write a(n) **phenomenon** about my life as the adopted child of a millionaire.

    _____

10. Since the police had **assimilated** me to the chair, I could not reach into my pocket to use my phone.

    _____

11. Haven't I always **allotted** your artistic talents, buying you lessons and instruments and such?

    _____

12. Kendra hopes to **instill** the other climbers when they stop to rest.

    _____

13. The wedding ceremony was so **ornate**; I swear I had seen it a hundred times before.

    _____

14. In the hospital, there was a(n) **deceptive** supply of pills.

    _____

15. It is a myth that Cuba is a safe **theme** for criminals.

    _____

7E Pick the Winner

Circle the word that best fits into the sentence. Then write a sentence below that uses the word you didn't pick in a meaningful way.

1. I was planning a Hawaiian (**themed OR shackled**) party.

2. _____

3. Candace, an Olympic skier, hopes to (**instill OR surpass**) previous speed records.

4. _____

5. Our new teacher **(allotted OR instilled)** us each three free homework passes for the semester.

6. _____

7. It was once a trend to have a **(bountiful OR conventional)** collection of Beanie Babies.

8. _____

9. One of the most interesting books I've read is the **(memoir OR haven)** of Miles Davis.

10. _____

7F Draw the Relationships

In each grouping of eight words below, draw straight lines between the synonyms (words that mean similar things) and squiggly lines between any antonyms (words that mean nearly opposite things). Every word should have at least one line connected to it. Some may have more.

1

assimilate   standard

allot   divide

adapt   huge

bountiful   conventional

2

foster   implant

deceptive   instill

honest   neglect

safe place   haven

3

occurrence   ornate

restrain   shackle

memoir   autobiography

plain   phenomenon

4

theme   fall back

sublime   unifying idea

amazing   surpass

bountiful   not enough

7G Understanding What You Read

Read the passage below. Then answer the questions.

Mo walked through the <u>ornate</u> halls, staring up at the detailed windows and walls. He couldn't help thinking that there had to be some mistake. It just wasn't <u>conventional</u> for a fourteen-year-old to inherit a house like this from a relative he hardly knew. Of course, he knew that his Aunt Josephine had always liked him, but this much?

Mo looked around the house, examining the curtains inlaid with gold fabric. He kicked off his shoes and ran his toes through the carpet. This, he thought to himself, was the most <u>sublime</u> feeling he'd ever experienced.

He glanced outside the window. The garden outside was breathtaking, with a stone walkway leading down through the lawn. The plants were <u>bountiful</u>: Large trees stood guard like obedient soldiers, and vines snaked their way up the high brick walls that surrounded the estate. What could possibly <u>surpass</u> this? Mo wondered. As he walked on, Mo ran his fingers over the back of a chair, noticing that the chair's arms resembled snakes. He gazed down a hall, and it seemed endless. It was almost like looking into outer space. A strange feeling came over him. Instead of feeling elated over this <u>phenomenon</u>, this absolute miracle of inheriting a house at his age, Mo began to get scared.

Suddenly, instead of feeling like a prince in a palace, Mo felt as though he were alone in a horrible dream. The staircase that had taken his breath away a minute ago suddenly <u>instilled</u> a sense of impending dread. The sun streaming through the skylight only <u>fostered</u> his fear: The fear that someone, somewhere was watching his every step.

He backed up slowly toward the door, as if he were waiting for a horror movie <u>theme</u> to start playing. He hardly breathed, as if every breath of air would <u>shackle</u> him further to the house. With his heart pounding, he stepped outside the door, into the fresh air and the warm, waiting sunlight.

1. The passage suggests that the house is
(A) cheap
(B) dirty
(C) clean
(D) expensive

2. According to the text, Mo goes from feeling
(A) overwhelmed to feeling fearful
(B) apprehensive to feeling deceived
(C) happy to feeling sublime
(D) excited to feeling scared

3. In the third paragraph, when Mo wonders "what could possibly surpass this," he means
(A) what could possibly be scarier than this
(B) what could possibly be more expensive than this
(C) what could possibly be more amazing than this
(D) what could possibly occur later in time

4. The final line of the story leads us to believe that Mo
(A) is about to get killed
(B) may have been imagining things
(C) was having a nightmare
(D) is scared of sunlight

5. The word "theme" is used in the last paragraph to mean
(A) music
(B) subject
(C) idea
(D) game

7H Thinking Creatively

Answer each question below. Don't be afraid to think creatively.

1. Why do you think evil Transformers were named **Decepticons**?

    _____

2. Describe a game show called *Assimilate that Man!*

    _____

3. What is the most **ornate** birthday cake you have ever seen?

    _____

4.   What is the most bizarre **phenomenon** you've ever heard of?

    _____

5.   Where in the world do you think has the most **sublime** views?

    _____

Word Breakdown

Deceive comes from the Latin *de* ("from") and *capere* ("to take"). When you deceive someone, you take from them. *Deceive* is just one of many words that mean to trick or mislead. *Deceit* usually involves lying or hiding the truth. *Betray* means that someone violated your trust in a major way: He betrayed us by telling the bully where we were hiding. *Mislead* means to lead in the wrong direction, either physically or mentally: It's easy to *mislead* a young kid into thinking that the sun revolves around the Earth. If you *dupe* someone, you are taking advantage of how dumb or naive they are: We were *duped* by the scalper into paying $300 for two tickets. To *bamboozle* is to trick using artful persuasion. *Double-cross* implies breaking a promise: The robber *double-crossed* his friend.

Unit 8 - Battle of Brooklyn

8A Introduction

The first few battles of the American Revolution went extremely well for the Americans. The Battle of Bunker Hill had shown the British just how hard these poor American farmers could fight. The British left Boston and sailed north to prepare. The American army (called the Continental army at the time) was led by General George Washington. He knew the British would attack New York City next, so he led his troops to Brooklyn to build forts. The British did indeed land in New York, but they had many more troops than Washington had expected, and they were able to fight past the American forts by sneaking through an unguarded trail.

Washington was faced with a tough decision: attempt to make a stand against a larger, better trained and equipped army, or retreat. Some say that winners never quit. Washington showed that there's a big difference between quitting and retreating.

8B Song Lyrics

This is the Battle of Brooklyn,
It's going down.
Know when to hold 'em and fold 'em,
And so we're rolling out.
You know that we're supposed to be colder than the south,
The flow is so golden they're like, "Oh wow."

So we signed the Declaration of Independence,
And it made Britain angry and **incensed**.
But it's a policy, an American **doctrine**:
If you don't let us vote, don't come a-knockin'.
But they came with their guns and their guns and their bombs,
And a fleet of ships, over a hundred strong.
It was hard though, they hit us up with an **embargo**,
And wouldn't let us trade our cargo.

We got cut like a barber, they surrounded New York Harbor,
And wouldn't let us trade or **barter**.
The ships were clouds that **forebode** a storm,
Told us of the war that was going to go on.
We had built forts and **fortified** them,
Made them strong to defend like a porcupine's skin.
Only problem: In Brooklyn we forgot a section,
That's a **defect**, or imperfection in the plan.
And they had more men than we did,
Even blind people could see we would be defeated.
They marched up with 34,000 troops,
That's a **formidable** army and scary too.
Plus our **inventory** ran so low,
The army had less ammo than Rambo.
We were **susceptible** to attacks, easily affected,
The huge fort we built up? They wrecked it.

barter / defect / dispatch / doctrine / embargo / flustered / foreboding / formidable / fortify / gaunt / haggard / incense / inventory / overt / susceptible

Hook

We sent a **dispatch**, which is a message,
To General George, like we need some help, kid.
We hadn't eaten, and our faces were **gaunt**,
Extremely thin and bony, and we're hating to march.
Our **haggard** faces showed our exhaustion,
Like, "The Brits didn't fight this hard in Boston!"
But George knew it was time to retreat,
So he waited till one night, when the Brits were asleep.

He started sending rowboats of Americans,
Across to Manhattan, the island.
We tried not to be **overt**, not obvious,
But the sun was coming up, and soon we'd all be dust.
But luck shined brighter than the sun did,
A fog rolled in thick as a rug is.
We escaped in the mist, and the British missed,
They couldn't see us from their British ships.

We lost the battle, yes, but Washington proved,
That in trouble he didn't get **flustered** or confused.
This is the lesson, get the picture like Kodak:
Know when to push on, and when to pull back.

Hook

8C Words Defined

Below you'll find each vocabulary word that was used in the song. Each word is followed by the part of speech, a simple definition and a meaningful sentence. Some words will also have synonyms, antonyms and other forms of the word listed.

1. barter (verb) to trade

At recess, the boys will often *barter* their baseball cards with one another.

2. defect (noun) an imperfection or fault

The toy cow was supposed to "moo" when his tail was pulled, but it had a *defect* and made no sound at all.
Other forms: *Defect* can also be a verb meaning "to leave, desert or abandon," as in: The man tried to *defect* from his country because the ruler was a harsh dictator.

3. dispatch (verb) to send off or away

The police will *dispatch* over a hundred volunteers to help search the nearby woods and fields for the missing child.
Other forms: A *dispatch* can also be a noun meaning "a message," as in: The soldier delivered the important *dispatch*.

4. doctrine (noun) a principle, position or belief system that is taught

The speech was full of religious *doctrine*, so I was bored and confused at the same time.
Synonyms: theory, belief, dogma
Other forms: If you are taught a *doctrine* until you believe it, you have been *indoctrinated* (verb).

5. embargo (noun) a prohibition or restriction, usually of trade

Because the government announced an *embargo* of all Cuban goods, I couldn't let the ship come in to dock.

6. flustered (adj) put into a state of confusion

The lawyer was so *flustered* by the judge's remarks that he accidentally knocked his glass of water on the floor.
Synonyms: distraught, rattled
Antonyms: clearheaded, composed

7. foreboding (adj) menacing; indicating something bad is coming

The huge waves and strong winds were a *foreboding* sign that a hurricane was brewing off the coast.
Other forms: *Foreboding* can also be a noun meaning "a prophesy." Also, clouds might *forebode* (verb) a storm if they indicate a storm is coming.

8. formidable (adj) causing fear or admiration

Even though Jasper was less than five feet tall, he was a *formidable* opponent in the boxing world.
Synonyms: impressive, mighty, daunting

9. fortify (verb) to make strong; to protect against an attack

Tony decided to *fortify* his sagging roof by adding two pillars.

10. gaunt (adj) thin and bony

The only survivor from the shipwreck looked *gaunt* after being stranded on an island with little food for three weeks.
Synonyms: skinny, bony

11. haggard (adj) worn and wild-looking

The travelers had *haggard* faces after flying for more than twenty hours without sufficient leg room or a meal.
Synonyms: fatigued, exhausted, ashen

12. incense (verb) to make extremely angry; infuriate

Gary was *incensed* when he received an F on his math final exam because he had studied for two solid weeks.
Other forms: *Incense* (verb) is also the name of the perfumed sticks you can buy to make your room smell good.

barter / defect / dispatch / doctrine / embargo / flustered / foreboding / formidable / fortify / gaunt / haggard / incense / inventory / overt / susceptible

---

13. inventory (noun) a supply of goods or materials

The bookstore had plenty of *inventory* – they had crates and crates of books – they just didn't have anyone to sell them to.
Other forms: *Inventory* is also sometimes used as a verb meaning "to take stock of, " as in: As a waitress, I had to *inventory* the ketchup, mustard, salt and pepper at the end of my shift.

14. overt (adj) open and observable; obvious

Billy made *overt* attempts to be exceptionally well behaved around the holidays.
Antonyms: hidden, sneaky, covert

15. susceptible (adj) easily influenced or affected

The premature baby was *susceptible* to colds, sicknesses, and infection.
Antonyms: resistant

8D Fix the Mistake

Each of the sentences below has a mistake. The wrong vocabulary words have been used, so the sentences don't make sense. Rewrite each sentence using the correct vocabulary word from this unit.

1. The model immediately noticed the **embargo** in the evening gown, even though it was very tiny.

   _____

2. By **dispatching** with each other for various items, the Native Americans were introduced to different types of tools, foods and musical instruments.

   _____

3. The hostages were completely **overt** from being given only bread and water for two months straight.

   _____

4. Only **haggard** water polo teams made it to the state championship meet.

   _____

5. The **foreboding** babysitter was pulling her hair out because she couldn't get the triplets to stop crying.

   _____

6. The restaurant manager ordered me to count our **doctrine** of ice cream toppings.

   _____

7. Many homeless people are **fortified** to catching colds and the flu in the winter since they live on the streets.

    _____

8. China placed a total **inventory** on all American-made products.

    _____

9. It **flusters** me so much when drivers tailgate me that I often scream at them.

    _____

10. Diana tried to keep her feelings hidden, but it was the most **susceptible** display of affection I had ever seen.

    _____

11. After the marathon, the runners looked **formidable** and in need of hot showers.

    _____

12. Nothing is more **gaunt** to a soldier walking through a village than the sound of absolute silence.

    _____

13. New York City was forced to **barter** all of its police officers during the riots.

    _____

14. The small country was so isolated that it created its own unique religious **defect**.

    _____

15. The cotton tent had been **flustered** with nylon so that it wouldn't rip.

    _____

8E Pick the Winner

Circle the word that best fits into the sentence. Then write a sentence below that uses the word you didn't pick in a meaningful way.

1. He was (**susceptible OR overt**) to having his feelings hurt on a regular basis because he was extremely sensitive.

2. _____

3. As a beginning driver, I was (**flustered OR dispatched**) by the cat darting out in front of my car.

4. _____

barter / defect / dispatch / doctrine / embargo / flustered / foreboding / formidable / fortify / gaunt / haggard / incense / inventory / overt / susceptible

5. The government placed an **(inventory OR embargo)** on any products made by children in foreign countries.

6. _____

7. The **(foreboding OR haggard)** clouds made the bride nervous since her wedding and reception were being held outdoors.

8. _____

9. I cried when I saw the **(gaunt OR formidable)** little boy in the orphanage because he looked hungry and lonely.

10. _____

8F Draw the Relationships

In each grouping of eight words below, draw straight lines between the synonyms (words that mean similar things) and squiggly lines between any antonyms (words that mean nearly opposite things). Every word should have at least one line connected to it. Some may have more.

1
trade   principle that is taught
send off   doctrine
barter   imperfection
defect   dispatch

2
weaken   fortify
embargo   foreboding
ban   favorable
confused   flustered

3
gaunt   haggard
formidable   mighty
anger   healthy
thin   incense

4
stock of goods   susceptible
inventory   incense
overt   perfume
inaccessible   hidden

8G Understanding What You Read

Read the passage below. Then answer the questions.

In March of 1776, after the yearlong Siege of Boston, the British fleet set sail for Canada to regroup and reorganize. General George Washington, expecting the British to attack New York City next, marched his troops to Manhattan and Brooklyn to <u>fortify</u> their position by building forts.

The British did just as Washington expected, sailing for New York Harbor and unloading many of their troops on Staten Island, between New Jersey and Brooklyn. However, Washington hadn't anticipated the size of the British army. More British soldiers had sailed from England, and they had also hired German mercenary soldiers to fight. In all, the British commanded a truly <u>formidable</u> army: They sent some 34,000 troops to New York. Washington had his forts, but he only had 9,000 men. Many of them were farmers who had left their farms to help. Having just marched from Boston with very little food, they were already <u>haggard</u>, their faces <u>gaunt</u> with exhaustion.

Things turned bad for the Americans when a British spy discovered a weakness in the American line. At night, the British marched through the weakly guarded Jamaica pass and came up on a group of Americans from the side. Those Americans fought back, but most of the soldiers were killed. The American soldiers pulled back to forts in Brooklyn Heights, dangerously close to the East River. Washington took <u>inventory</u> of the situation. He realized that if the British pressed on and pinned the Americans against the river, Washington and his men might have no choice but to surrender.

Therefore, during the night of August 30th, Washington decided that he had to evacuate Brooklyn and bring his soldiers to Manhattan. But moving 9,000 soldiers across the river wouldn't be easy. After all, there was no Brooklyn Bridge in 1776. Instead, they had big rowboats. But the process did not go as quickly as Washington had hoped, and by sunrise many men were still in Brooklyn, dangerously open to enemy attack. The first rays of light coming over the horizon were as <u>foreboding</u> as thunderclouds to the soldiers that morning. Luckily, just as the sun came up, an unusually thick fog rolled into New York Harbor, hiding the Americans from view.

Washington did retreat, eventually allowing the British to occupy all of New York City, which they held for the rest of the war. But his move caught the British completely by surprise, and his technique earned him praise from both Americans and the British. Certainly, his luck and smarts helped the Americans win their war of independence.

1. Which of the following describes Washington's knowledge of what the British would do after the Siege of Boston?
(A) He knew where they would sail, and he realized how big the army was.
(B) He knew where they would sail, but he didn't realize how big the army was.
(C) He didn't know where they would sail, but he realized how big the army was.
(D) He didn't know where they would sail, and he didn't realize how big the army was.

2. Which of the following mottos best fits the George Washington described in this passage?
(A) We will shell them on the beaches...we shall never surrender.
(B) Live and let live.
(C) You have to know when to strike and when to retreat.
(D) The only thing we have to fear is fear itself.

3. When "Washington took inventory of the situation," he
(A) scattered his troops
(B) created fortifications
(C) requested back up
(D) gathered information of his current situation

4. According to the text, the British army was made up of
(A) British soldiers and hired troops from Germany
(B) British soldiers and Americans who opposed independence
(C) English and British soldiers
(D) Ships and cannons, mostly

5. Why was the sunrise described as "foreboding" in this passage?
(A) because sunlight makes it easier to travel by boat
(B) because sunshine might make the British troops lazy
(C) because the sun would expose the American forts
(D) because the sun would let the British see the American retreat

8H Thinking Creatively

Answer each question below. Don't be afraid to think creatively.

1.   If you could **barter** one item from your bedroom for something you've always wanted, what would that item be?

_____

2.   What is the most **foreboding** thing you can think of?

_____

3.   What is the [insert your name here] **Doctrine**?

_____

4.   Why should poverty **incense** us?

_____

5.   Describe a TV show named *Susceptible to Laughter*.

_____

Word Breakdown

Incense, as a noun, is that sweet-scented perfume stick that you can burn to smell flavors such as "apple fantasy" and "Egyptian musk." The word *incense* comes from the Latin *insensum*, which literally means "something that's burnt." Thus, *incendiary* means "causing fire," and if something *incenses* you, it metaphorically sets you on fire: You get upset.

The word *sense* has nothing to do with *incense* except that they rhyme. *Sense* comes from the Latin *sensus*, meaning "to perceive." Still, Spike Lee plays with the two words together in his movie *Mo' Better Blues*. In a famous scene, one character complains to another that, "It makes no sense. It *incenses* me that our own people don't realize our own heritage."

Unit 9 - Back in the Jam

9A Introduction

Hip-hop was born in the Bronx in the seventies. It came out of parties – street parties thrown by young DJs who knew they could get the crowd into it if they mixed beats and spit rhymes on the mic. They say there are four pillars to hip-hop: DJing (scratching and mixing), MCing (rapping), graffiti, and break dancing. But from a few guys spinning on their heads and tagging walls in the Bronx, hip-hop has become an international business worth billions of dollars. Still, when the sun goes down, hip-hop really lives on the block, right around the corner.

9B Song Lyrics

We put the OOP - OOP back in the jam.

We agreed about music, we're in **accord**,
Are we in a Jetta? Naw, we're in an Accord.
Please excuse my **antics**, my playful tricks,
And Excuse My Dear Aunt Sally, yeah she's kind of sick.
There's four parts or **components** in Hip-Hop,
Graffiti, break-dancing, DJing, and rapping.
We made the **transition** and change from scatting,
From "Skoobiddybeebop" to "you know we rock."

Some say graffiti, it **defaces** a wall,
Spoils its appearance, and changes it all.
Others say it's not harmful, it's **benign**,
In fact, it makes a boring wall look just fine.
You're a **rational** person, think and reason,
You be the judge: Tell me what you're believing.
Rap started in America, up in the Bronx,
Then spread through the world, bringing us the funk.

Hook

Hip-Hop turned into a **bonanza**, oh my,
A source of great wealth like a gold mine.
If it's an **infinite**, never-ending source of wealth,
We better spread it out, never keep it to ourselves.
Let me **cite** an example, refer to some proof:
Ludacris gives money back to the schools.
'Cause Luda realized rapping can be **lucrative**,
Very profitable, if you're good with it.

That's an idea or a **concept** that works,
So a million lazy rappers emerge.
But it's not an **enigma,** or a riddle,
Lazy people get played quickly like fiddles.
We don't give in to it, **succumb** to greed,
It's not about money, this is fun to me.

Unit 9

accord / antics / benign / bonanza / cite / component / concept / deface / enigma / infinite / lucrative / rational / serene / succumb / transition

Maybe Cash Rules Everything Around Me – CREAM,
But I stay calm and **serene**.

Hook

9C Words Defined

Below you'll find each vocabulary word that was used in the song. Each word is followed by the part of speech, a simple definition and a meaningful sentence. Some words will also have synonyms, antonyms and other forms of the word listed.

1. accord (noun) an agreement, usually a formal one.

The two countries reached an *accord* to end the war.
Other forms: Two ideas can be in *accordance* (noun) or in *accord* (noun) when similar. One idea can be *according* (adverb) to another.

2. antics (noun) playful or mischievous tricks, pranks or shenanigans

My mother was late for work and in no mood for my brother's *antics* as he tied his shoelaces.

3. benign (adj) 1. not harmful 2. kind and generous (of a person)

1. You think swallowing a little dirt is bad, but it's actually *benign*. 2. The *benign* ruler sent out birthday cards to all her subjects.

4. bonanza (noun) a rich harvest or a sudden good fortune

This year's crop of tomatoes was a *bonanza* for the local farmers.
Synonyms: gold mine, windfall

5. cite (verb) to quote something as an authority

Lawyers often *cite* police documents to prove their case.
Other forms: When a writer *cites* a source in an essay, it is a *citation* (noun).

6. component (noun) a part or piece of a greater whole

Learning how to write introductions is just one *component* of writing an entire essay.
Synonyms: element, ingredient, constituent

7. concept (noun) an idea

Dividing exponents was a difficult *concept* for the honor students to grasp.
Other forms: An idea that is not yet completed is just *conceptual* (adj.).

8. deface (verb) to spoil the appearance of

Those students who *deface* the locker room walls with graffiti will spend their weekend scrubbing it clean.
Synonyms: to mar, vandalize

9. enigma (noun) a puzzling situation or person

I can't figure out what motivates Darnell; he's an *enigma* to me.

10. infinite (adj) going on forever; having no boundaries

It looked as though there were an *infinite* amount of daisies in the meadow next to my house.
Antonyms: limited, finite
Other forms: The astronauts hope to explore a tiny part of the *infinity* (noun) that is space.

11. lucrative (adj) very profitable

Luckily, my stockbroker made a *lucrative* investment with my money, so I will be able to retire early.

12. rational (adj) reasonable, sensible

The crooks knew they needed to stay *rational* and not make any crazy decisions.
Synonyms: calm, level-headed
Antonyms: illogical, irrational

13. serene (adj) calm and peaceful

The grandparents liked the *serene* atmosphere of the resort, as opposed to the loud and noisy beach area.
Other forms: *Serenity* (noun) overcame me as I sat silently next to the still lake.

14. succumb (verb) to yield, surrender, give in

The protesters did not *succumb* to the spraying of pepper spray and rubber bullets.
Antonyms: conquer, dominate

15. transition (noun) a movement from one form, state, style, or place to another

The twenty-second century will witness a *transition* from automobiles to flying "aero-cars."
Other forms: *Transition* can also be used as a verb: Bill *transitioned* from selling bikes to selling cars.

9D Fix the Mistake

Each of the sentences below has a mistake. The wrong vocabulary words have been used, so the sentences don't make sense. Rewrite each sentence using the correct vocabulary word from this unit.

1.   It was often difficult for hyper Jake to **antics** from PE class to reading class.

        _____

2.   The pumpkin patch was a(n) **accord** of different sizes and shapes to choose from.

        _____

3.   Frances **cites** her desk in math class with drawings of roses and guitars.

accord / antics / benign / bonanza / cite / component / concept / deface / enigma / infinite / lucrative / rational / serene / succumb / transition

4.   Crawling on my stomach under barbed wire was only one **concept** of the obstacle course.

      _____

5.   Thankfully, Josh's stomach tumor was **lucrative** and could be operated on immediately.

      _____

6.   At the maternity ward, it was very **infinite**, since only two babies had been born and they were both sleeping.

      _____

7.   During the earthquake, the teacher remained **benign** so that she could give clear instructions for her students to follow.

      _____

8.   My little sister's **enigmas** in the grocery store were so embarrassing that we had to leave our full cart and go home.

      _____

9.   The **component** between my parents and me was that if I got all A's and B's on my report card, they would buy me a new car of my choice.

      _____

10.   After pulling my dad over for speeding, the police officer **succumbed** the traffic code to prove he had broken the law.

      _____

11.   There was a(n) **serene** amount of balloons at the birthday party.

      _____

12.   Although she was surrounded by sugary foods, Casey vowed to stick to her diet and not to **deface** to the cravings.

      _____

13.   After collecting over three thousand Beanie Babies, I discovered it was not a very **rational** investment since they were not worth any more than I'd paid for them .

      _____

14.   Chemistry was by far the most difficult **bonanza** to understand in high school.

      _____

15.   It was a total **transition**: The only person who could have committed the crime had a bulletproof alibi.

_____

9E Pick the Winner

Circle the word that best fits into the sentence. Then write a sentence below that uses the word you didn't pick in a meaningful way.

1.   Five countries reached an **(accord OR antic)**, agreeing to not bomb each other during the holiday season.

2.   _____

3.   The **(enigma OR transition)** from childhood to adolescence is a bumpy one at times.

4.   _____

5.   The monastery had a very **(serene OR rational)** atmosphere, so I felt very calm during my visit.

6.   _____

7.   In order to be initiated into the gang, the recruits had to **(succumb OR deface)** a wall with graffiti.

8.   _____

9.   One **(component OR bonanza)** of winning the board game was to collect as many of your opponent's game pieces as possible.

10.   _____

9F Draw the Relationships

In each grouping of eight words below, draw straight lines between the synonyms (words that mean similar things) and squiggly lines between any antonyms (words that mean nearly opposite things). Every word should have at least one line connected to it. Some may have more.

1

lottery win   disagreement

accord   foolishness

harmful   antics

benign   bonanza

accord / antics / benign / bonanza / cite / component / concept / deface / enigma / infinite / lucrative / rational / serene / succumb / transition

2

	element	idea	
cite			concept
reference			deface
	vandalize	component	

3

	rational	wild	
infinite			profitable
lucrative			illogical
	serene	measurable	

4

	stay strong	change	
succumb			infinite
puzzle			endless
	enigma	transition	

9G Understanding What You Read

Read the passage below. Then answer the questions.

Ashley tried to justify her <u>antics</u> to her friends. "Come on, Jas," she whined. "It wasn't that bad." Jasmine looked at her like she was crazy.

"You're not even acting <u>rational</u> lately," she said. "You're acting all weird, like you're trying to get everyone's attention or something."

"I am not." Ashley looked confused, as though she couldn't believe what her friend was saying. "You can't prove that."

Jasmine started to <u>cite</u> examples: the time Ashley <u>defaced</u> the school wall with lipstick, the time she climbed on Ms. Swanson's car and started screaming about how she hated football. Ashley nodded her head. "Alright, that's a little weird," she agreed. "I guess. But it's all <u>benign</u> stuff. I didn't hurt anybody."

"It's not <u>benign</u>! You've been my best friend for years. You said our friendship was <u>infinite</u> and we were going to be like that forever. Now all of a sudden, you're getting strange and changing and all that." Jasmine looked down, trying not to <u>succumb</u> to the sadness that was overwhelming her.

Ashley touched Jasmine on the shoulder and looked at her with a <u>serene</u>, peaceful expression. "I'm sorry," she said. "I know it's been weird. But middle school's weird. Everybody does weird stuff."

"Yeah, but you don't have to," Jasmine said.

"I know." Ashley hugged her. "But you can be more supportive." Jasmine nodded. Having reached their <u>accord</u>, the two friends walked to class.

1. Jasmine accuses Ashley of
(A) being mean
(B) paying too much attention to boys
(C) letting her grades slip
(D) trying to be the center of attention

2. Ashley "not acting rationally" suggests she was
(A) not acting sensibly
(B) acting logically
(C) not acting silly enough
(D) not being friendly

3. The "accord" that Ashley and Jasmine reach at the end of the passage is probably an agreement to
(A) disagree
(B) split up as friends
(C) be supportive friends again
(D) hug and go to class

4. The text suggests that middle school is a time when
(A) many enigmas come around every corner
(B) students are benign
(C) girls and boys don't get along
(D) some people act strangely

5. A synonym for Ashley's "antics" would be
(A) bad grades
(B) money
(C) shenanigans
(D) temper tantrums

9H Thinking Creatively

Answer each question below. Don't be afraid to think creatively.

1. Would you rather live under a **benign** king or a boring President?

    _____

2. Rewrite this sentence using synonyms: Sally **cited** several sayings.

    _____

3. What is something that you consider **infinite**?

    _____

4. Describe a **lucrative** business you could start at school.

    _____

5. What is an **enigma** that is unsolved?

    _____

accord / antics / benign / bonanza / cite / component / concept / deface / enigma / infinite / lucrative / rational / serene / succumb / transition

Word Breakdown

Enigma comes from Latin *aenigma* ("riddle"), which comes from *ainos*, the Greek word for "fable." In today's usage, an enigma can be either a riddle ("What can you catch but can't throw?") or a mystery ("Who really shot John F. Kennedy?"). The Prime Minister of England during World War II, Winston Churchill, was once asked what he thought Russia would do after the war. He answered: "I cannot forecast to you the action of Russia. It is a riddle wrapped in a mystery inside an enigma."

Unit 10 - Changes

10A Introduction

This song is written about a serious issue - drunk driving, which is a major problem in America. Each year, on average, more than 15,000 people are killed and 250,000 people are injured in drunk driving car accidents. Clearly, this is something that has to change. The narrator in this song knows that all too well.

10B Song Lyrics

Life changes easily,
Ain't never what it seems to be.
Better hold it like you own it,
'Cause you could lose it in a moment.

Ice Tea in my hand, ice cubes were melting,
The weather was so hot, it's **sweltering**.
Nighttime, the right time to take a drive,
But my situation turned terrible and **dire**.
The night was **eventful**, full of events,
If I hadn't been lucky, I could have been dead.
A car swerved, I could see the lights,
They were **luminous**, and shining bright.

I hit the breaks, and the sound was **strident**,
It sounded like a baby crying.
This guy's car smashed into me,
Crunched under the door, I could barely breathe.
The pain was **excruciating**,
So intense, and wasn't fading.
This guy hadn't acted **conscientiously**,
He wasn't thinking carefully, you feel me?

Hook

Now this guy had been drinking heavily,
So, the ambulance came and handled me.
The cops arrived, and they tested him,
Then they **apprehended** and arrested him.
The judge had the power and **authority**
To throw him in jail for just forty weeks.
I wish it was a **millennium**, a thousand years,
One for each time that I cried a tear.

They should have let him **languish** in jail,
Sit there, become weak and frail.
To this day, it still **rankles** me,

Irritates me that they set him free.
What's to say that it won't **recur**?
Occur again, it might be worse.
Now I need a wheelchair to **facilitate**
and make movement easy, you feel me?

For all the people that drink and drive,
Blink your eyes, cause you either think or die.
I hope this **deters** and prevents you
From doing something that you can't undo...

Hook

10C Words Defined

Below you'll find each vocabulary word that was used in the song. Each word is followed by the part of speech, a simple definition and a meaningful sentence. Some words will also have synonyms, antonyms and other forms of the word listed.

1. apprehend (verb) to arrest or take into custody

Brian would do anything to *apprehend* his wife's murderer.
Other forms: *Apprehend* is also a verb meaning "to perceive or understand," as in: It was difficult for the kindergartners to *apprehend* the idea of death when the class hamster suddenly died.

2. authority (noun) 1. power to influence how others act or think 2. someone who has power or knowledge

Umpires have the *authority* to eject players and coaches from the game. 2. Einstein was an *authority* when it came to physics.
Other forms: You can *authorize* (verb) something if you give your permission for it to happen.

3. conscientious (adj) careful; well thought-out

When my dad and I wrestle in the living room, we have to be very *conscientious* of my baby sister so we do not hurt her.
Antonyms: careless, inattentive, negligent
Other forms: Your *conscience* (noun) is your inner sense of what is right and wrong.

4. deter (verb) to prevent or discourage from proceeding

Karina tried to *deter* her little brother from eating the last cupcake by licking all the frosting off of it.
Antonyms: to encourage, persuade

5. dire (adj) desperate; terrible

Two of the soccer players were in *dire* need of a water break during the game, since the temperature was over one hundred degrees.
Synonyms: urgent, critical, pressing

6. eventful (adj) full of events; important

The day Lisa was born was the most *eventful* day of her father's life.

7. excruciating (adj) extremely intense or painful

The football player was in *excruciating* pain after being tackled by four defensive lineman.
Antonyms: pleasant, soothing, enjoyable

8. facilitate (verb) to assist or make easier

The therapist tried to *facilitate* a conversation between the unhappy husband and wife.
Other forms: The *facilitator* (noun) led the meeting.

9. languish (verb) to become weak; lose health

The lady *languished* once her partner died.
Synonyms: to weaken, deteriorate

10. luminous (adj) shining and bright

The stage was *luminous* from all the spotlights cast upon it.
Antonyms: dark, dim, obscure

11. millennium (noun) a period of one thousand years

Chelsea felt like a *millennium* had passed before she got her cell phone back from her parents.

12. rankle (verb) to cause irritation or resentment

It *rankles* our PE teacher for days when students openly disrespect him.
Antonyms: to calm, pacify, soothe

13. recur (verb) to repeat or happen again

Gail's nightmare would *recur* night after night, so she eventually refused to go to sleep.
Other forms: There was a *recurrence* (noun) of chicken pox in the elementary school. There was a *recurring* (adj) theme in the books they read this semester: death.

14. strident (adj) harsh or grating, as in a sound

A *strident* tone echoes in the house every time my sister practices her violin.
Antonyms: soft, silent, calm

15. swelter (verb) to be uncomfortably hot

The kids are going to *swelter* out by the pool all day since there is no shade or overhang to keep them cool.

apprehend / authority / conscientious / deter / dire / eventful / excruciating / facilitate / languish / luminous / millennium / rankle / recur / strident / swelter

10D Fix the Mistake

Each of the sentences below has a mistake. The wrong vocabulary words have been used, so the sentences don't make sense. Rewrite each sentence using the correct vocabulary word from this unit.

1. Luckily, the police were able to **deter** the criminal before he was able to leave the country.

   _____

2. Mrs. Dunker's **millennium** in the classroom was clear with her relentless use of detention slips.

   _____

3. After being hit by the car, the dog was in **eventful** pain.

   _____

4. Teenagers can really **facilitate** their parents by refusing to speak to them.

   _____

5. Brandon was a very **dire** babysitter because he renewed his CPR and first aid training annually.

   _____

6. My hiking partner was convinced that he was going to **recur** without his water bottle.

   _____

7. A metal bat hitting a ball makes a more **excruciating** sound than a wooden bat.

   _____

8. The sports spectators were all **apprehending** in the bleacher seats because there was no shade.

   _____

9. For Janice, who hated school, it felt like a(n) **authority** until she graduated.

   _____

10. The pool looked **strident** at night with all of its lights turned on.

   _____

11. The police officer's first night on the job was a(n) **conscientious** one with two murders, a burglary and a car chase.

   _____

12. Jason tried to **languish** his best friend from talking in class so he wouldn't get in any more trouble.

   _____

13. Five swimmers were in **luminous** need of being rescued by the lifeguards because the current had started to sweep them out to sea.

   _____

14. As an event planner, it was Jocelyn's job to be able to **swelter** numerous activities at once.

   _____

15. After I had the hiccups for over two hours, they finally stopped, and I prayed they would not **rankle**.

   _____

10E Pick the Winner

Circle the word that best fits into the sentence. Then write a sentence below that uses the word you didn't pick in a meaningful way.

1. It was hard to **(deter OR rankle)** the toddler from touching the appetizers on the coffee table since they were at his eye level.

2. _____

3. The airplane delays, hotel problems and poor weather made for a(n) **(eventful OR luminous)** vacation.

4. _____

5. Lightning was **(recurring OR languishing)** so often that it was like daylight in the middle of the night.

6. _____

7. When Sonya got mad in class, she would slowly run her fingernails down the chalkboard and make a **(conscientious OR strident)** noise.

8. _____

9. New York is already planning the New Year's Eve bash for the next **(millennium OR authority)**.

10. _____

apprehend / authority / conscientious / deter / dire / eventful / excruciating / facilitate / languish / luminous / millennium / rankle / recur / strident / swelter

10F Draw the Relationships

In each grouping of eight words below, draw straight lines between the synonyms (words that mean similar things) and squiggly lines between any antonyms (words that mean nearly opposite things). Every word should have at least one line connected to it. Some may have more.

1

authority   conscientious

encourage   arrest

apprehend   power

negligent   deter

2

urgent   busy

dire   facilitate

soothing   assist

eventful   excruciating

3

millennium   dark

languish   a thousand years

waste away   luminous

make mad   rankle

4

sweat   pleasant

recur   conscientious

strident   repeat

careful   swelter

10G Understanding What You Read

Read the passage below. Then answer the questions.

Andre sat in the car in the <u>sweltering</u> August heat. Man, did he hate the waiting part of this job! Sometimes it would be quick, like an hour. But other times, he would have to sit on the stakeout for a whole night, or for three or four <u>excruciating</u> days, just waiting for something <u>eventful</u> to happen. Tonight, he thought, it might be a long wait, but if they could nab this one, it'd be his biggest bust.

Of course, to do that, all they had to do was catch the West Coast's biggest jewel thief red-handed. They wouldn't need to <u>apprehend</u> him; they just needed to get some photos that showed him coming out of the store. Sounded easy enough, but man, was it hot. Andre's old '89 Civic had a busted air conditioner, and he wasn't sure how long he could <u>languish</u> in the heat.

"Just a few more hours," he told himself. "He's coming out of there soon." He reminded himself how important this was. This would be the bust of the <u>millennium</u>! He thought of the promotion he'd undoubtedly get if he could just wait this one out: more money, more <u>authority</u>, maybe even a paid vacation somewhere. He rubbed his hands in anticipation.

Hours passed. Andre could see the sky slowly grow more <u>luminous</u>. It was still hot, and he couldn't believe he was still awake. He flipped around the radio, stared at the door, and waited for the slightest hint of movement. Every time he thought the door moved, he sat up and gripped the steering wheel of his car. He began to wonder if the guy was even in there at all. Impossible. He'd seen him go in. He had to be in there. Andre started shaking his head. He wasn't even that <u>conscientious</u> of his surroundings anymore. Was he losing his mind?

The door swung open. A tall man wearing a black suit poked his head out the door. He was carrying a large briefcase. Andre started snapping pictures.

1. In the first paragraph, the phrase "excruciating days" is used to mean that the days were
(A) easy and fun
(B) eventful and crazy
(C) boring and long
(D) interesting but painful

2. The text suggests that Andre was working as
(A) a professional thief
(B) an undercover detective
(C) a police chief
(D) night-shift worker

3. Andre was uncomfortable waiting because he was
(A) luminous
(B) sweltering
(C) conscientious
(D) apprehensive

4. The action in the last two paragraphs most likely takes place at what time of day?
(A) six in the morning
(B) two in the afternoon
(C) seven in the evening
(D) midnight

5. The end of the passage suggests that Andre
(A) arrests the thief
(B) begins to dream
(C) goes crazy
(D) gets what he needed

10H Thinking Creatively

Answer each question below. Don't be afraid to think creatively.

1. What do you think a **conscientious** objector to a war is?

    _____

2. Briefly describe a TV show called *Fish or Languish!*

    _____

3.   If someone said a comedy was **excruciating**, what do you think they'd mean?

_____

4.   Why is it so difficult for the FBI to **apprehend** the ten most wanted people in the U.S.?

_____

5.   If an author consulted you on a book she was writing about teenagers, what information would you be an **authority** on?

_____

Word Breakdown

A *decade* is ten years. A *century* is ten decades or one hundred years. A *millennium* is one hundred decades, ten centuries or one thousand years. So, what comes after millennium? Well, nothing. There is no specific word for 10 *millennia*. *Era* and *epoch* don't have a specific numerical value. An *eternity* is usually considered to be never ending, or infinite.

Millennium comes from Latin *mille* ("a thousand") and *annus* ("year," as in *annual*). The extra *ion* in million means "great," so a million is a "great thousand," now defined as a thousand thousand. A *millionaire* has at least a million dollars. There is no word for a person who has at least a thousand dollars; the word *millaire* doesn't really exist. McDonalds got creative and played around with words to advertise their Dollar Menu, though. They created the phrase *dollar menunaire* to describe a person who has at least one dollar and likes to live frugally.

Unit 11 - Two Bad Cousins

11A Introduction

These two comical cousins have a love/hate relationship. They're close, but they're also competitive. Each one has a distinct personality: Lulu is quiet, and Lee is over the top. Most of the time, they get along just fine.

11B Song Lyrics

My cousin Lee has a temper, he's **irascible**,
On the court, I'm like, "Yo! Pass the ball."
Aww naww, he's a ball hog,
So I launched a verbal attack, an **onslaught**.
"At some point, **eventually**, Lee,
You're going to need the rest of the team."
He didn't think much of me, **disdained** me,
He said, "Yo, girl, quit acting like a baby."

That's an **excerpt** from what he said to me,
He said more words that I won't repeat.
I t-t-t-t-tried to stay **indifferent**,
And act like I didn't care a little.
I told him I was **adept** for real,
I could hit threes, and I had real skills.
He didn't believe me, so I snatched the ball,
And dunked over him like an astronaut.

We're experts in the field, like connoisseurs.
Lee, only eats meat like a carnivore.
Lulu, let's clarify and clear it up,
We're just two bad cousins who will never stop.

My cousin Lulu wears a tall hat,
She has sneakers, thinks she's all that.
She'll believe any story,
I told her the word **gullible** wasn't even in the dictionary.
Oh, OK, that was a lie,
It was a test to see if she was **sage** and wise.
Lee is my **pseudonym,** my nickname,
My real name's Levar, I have a big chain.

My only problem is that my armpits
Smell like onions, they're so **pungent**.
I use gel in my hair to keep it **sleek** and smooth,
And I know the secret to life, it's simple, dude.
Just **renounce** vegetables, give 'em up,
I get the vitamins that I need from my Corn Pops.
Oh, that advice was not **profound**,
Like the kiddie pool, you see? Not too deep...

adept / clarify / connoisseur / disdain / excerpt / gullible / indifferent / irascible / onslaught / profound / pseudonym / pungent / renounce / sage / sleek

Hook

11C Song Lyrics

Below you'll find each vocabulary word that was used in the song. Each word is followed by the part of speech, a simple definition and a meaningful sentence. Some words will also have synonyms, antonyms and other forms of the word listed.

1. adept (adj) very skilled; expert

The juggler was so *adept* he actually juggled three chainsaws.

2. clarify (verb) to make clear or understandable

The senator asked the witness to *clarify* his earlier statement.
Synonyms: simplify, refine
Antonyms: confuse, complicate
Other forms: A *clarification* (noun) is what is given to you when you ask someone to *clarify* something.

3. connoisseur (noun) an expert in a specific field, such as art or food

My best friend was a *connoisseur* of Impressionistic art; he collected it.
Antonyms: amateur, novice

4. disdain (verb) to look down upon or hate

My PE teacher *disdained* lazy students and thought they weren't worth his time.
Synonyms: to hate, feel contempt for
Other forms: *Disdain* can also be a noun, as in: The proud poodle owner felt nothing but *disdain* for those owners who let their dogs get covered in mud.

5. excerpt (noun) a passage or selection from a book, film, song or the like

The author chose to read an *excerpt* from his best-selling novel, *Torture Chamber*.

6. gullible (adj) easily tricked or deceived

Nina was so *gullible* that she believed the roller coaster's loop was an illusion.
Synonyms: trusting, naive
Antonyms: suspicious, skeptical, wary

7. indifferent (adj) having no particular interest one way or the other

When it comes to my pain, she is totally *indifferent* and that increases the pain.
Antonyms: caring
Other forms: Kendra expressed her *indifference* (noun) to the musical by leaving halfway through.

8. irascible (adj) very irritable or easily angered

Most of the *irascible* old men at the rest home upset their nurses on a daily basis.
Synonyms: testy, cranky

9. onslaught (noun) a violent attack or a huge outpouring

There was an *onslaught* of mosquitoes during the barbecue, so we had to move the party indoors.

10. profound (adj) deep

The teacher was surprised to find that the class clown was such a *profound* thinker.
Antonyms: shallow

11. pseudonym (noun) a fake or alternate name

The author wanted to see if people liked his writing or him, so he wrote several books using a *pseudonym* to test that theory.
Synonyms: alias, false name, nickname

12. pungent (adj) sharp and powerful, usually smell or taste

Diane's remarks about Steve being a liar were as *pungent* as stinky cheese.
Antonyms: bland, mild

13. renounce (verb) to give up voluntarily

Sam told his father he hated him so much that he would *renounce* his inheritance of $200,000.
Synonyms: abandon

14. sage (adj) wise

Dave was known for his *sage* advice regarding the stock market.
Other forms: *Sage* is also a noun meaning "a wise person," as in: The *sage* warned that chaos would prevail unless the community started to work together.

15. sleek (adj) smooth, slick, shiny

Devin pulled up in a *sleek* new Corvette to pick up his prom date.
Antonyms: dull, rough

11D Fix the Mistake

Each of the sentences below has a mistake. The wrong vocabulary words have been used, so the sentences don't make sense. Rewrite each sentence using the correct vocabulary word from this unit.

1.   Dee is such a(n) **indifferent** soccer player that, although he's still a kid, he plays on an adult team.

   _____

2.   Deidre had to **renounce** the multistep directions for the art project so there would be no mistakes.

   _____

adept / clarify / connoisseur / disdain / excerpt / gullible / indifferent / irascible / onslaught / profound / pseudonym / pungent / renounce / sage / sleek

3. He was such a(n) **pseudonym** of food and wine that it was scary to cook dinner for him.

    _____

4. The bookie gave us **sleek** advice on which horses to bet on at the racetrack, and we won.

    _____

5. The **profound** smell of vinegar filled the kitchen as we dyed Easter eggs.

    _____

6. A(n) **excerpt** of moviegoers stormed the theater as the doors opened.

    _____

7. The **gullible** old lady was upset that someone had moved her cane from its normal resting place.

    _____

8. Big Kim had nothing but **connoisseur** for campers who killed spiders instead of releasing them back outside.

    _____

9. Harriet was so **adept** that she believed our story that Bigfoot had been captured and was on display at the local zoo.

    _____

10. Once accepted into the witness protection program, I had to assume a(n) **disdain,** so I chose Oprah Springer.

    _____

11. His **irascible** new haircut made him look like Elvis.

    _____

12. Once he didn't believe in the politician anymore, he **clarified** him at every chance he got.

    _____

13. For a first grader, he had some very **pungent** thoughts about life after death.

    _____

14. We were given only a short **onslaught** of the entire book to read, so I was left hanging as to how it ended.

    _____

15.   Everybody seemed to have very strong feelings on whether to impeach the President or not, but I just felt **sage** about the whole thing.

_____

11E Pick the Winner

Circle the word that best fits into the sentence. Then write a sentence below that uses the word you didn't pick in a meaningful way.

1.   There was a **(pungent OR profound)** smell coming out of the science lab where they were dissecting frogs.

2.   _____

3.   Our English teacher had us all write one essay during the year under a **(connoisseur OR pseudonym)** to prove to us that it was our writing we were getting graded on as opposed to who we were.

4.   _____

5.   Mimi was very **(gullible OR adept)** at fixing computers or anything to do with technology.

6.   _____

7.   The treasurer decided to **(renounce OR clarify)** his position on the board of directors since there was such controversy surrounding him.

8.   _____

9.   I was shocked to see the rich women treat the homeless people with such **(disdain OR excerpt)** when they passed them on the streets.

10.   _____

11F Draw the Relationships

In each grouping of eight words below, draw straight lines between the synonyms (words that mean similar things) and squiggly lines between any antonyms (words that mean nearly opposite things). Every word should have at least one line connected to it. Some may have more.

1

confuse   clarify

adept   disdain

hatred   skilled

amateur   connoisseur

adept / clarify / connoisseur / disdain / excerpt / gullible / indifferent / irascible / onslaught / profound / pseudonym / pungent / renounce / sage / sleek

2

	kind	indifferent	
excerpt			a selection
gullible			skeptical
	interested	irascible	

3

	shallow	profound	
onslaught			pungent
attack			bland
	nickname	pseudonym	

4

	keep	dull	
renounce			clarify
sage			smart
	simplify	sleek	

11G Understanding What You Read

Read the passage below. Then answer the questions.

James lined up at the starting line, thinking that he would easily win. "I'm more <u>adept</u> at running than anyone here," he thought. "There's no reason on earth why I shouldn't win."

Harlan lined up next. James saw him coming and groaned, wishing he could use a <u>pseudonym</u> and a disguise and not have to be next to him. Harlan was the perfect, popular kid who James had never liked. James thought he was always spouting off his <u>profound</u> opinions in class, like he was the smartest person to ever show up in a classroom. He was popular too, and <u>disdained</u> everyone who didn't run with his circle of friends.

Harlan nodded at James. James nodded back at him and put his eyes forward. He focused on the finish line one hundred yards down the track. Harlan looked over at James and smiled, then he scrunched up his face like he'd just smelled something particularly <u>pungent</u>. "I just thought I should <u>clarify</u> the instructions for you," Harlan said. "They fire the gun, and then I run you off the track."

"Keep talking," James said. "And when we start running, you can tell me whether I have anything stuck to the back of my shirt." The official called out, "Marks!" The two boys crouched down into their starting positions. The pistol fired and they took off. James imagined himself as a <u>sleek,</u> silvery bullet. He looked beside him and saw Harlan one step behind him.

The finish line was coming up quickly, when it all happened in an instant. James felt something snap at his foot. Harlan was trying to trip him! James took two large steps only to see Harlan fall on the ground, holding his ankle.

James felt strangely <u>indifferent</u> about Harlan's trouble. He crossed the finish line as an <u>onslaught</u> of classmates swarmed him. "See you next fall, Harlan," he whispered to himself.

1. Harlan's character can best be described as
(A) indifferent
(B) big
(C) boring
(D) mean

2. When James wishes he had a "pseudonym," he is wishing that
(A) he was a mean bully so he could beat up Harlan
(B) he had practiced running more
(C) he had a fake name
(D) he had taken karate lessons

3. According to the text, Harlan
(A) fears other people
(B) wishes others would leave him alone
(C) is the best runner at school
(D) sees others as inferior to him

4. James mentions "something on the back of my shirt" in order to
(A) get Harlan to take whatever it is off, so James can run faster
(B) tease Harlan
(C) make Harlan think he has a jet pack
(D) show Harlan that he has a better number on his shirt

5. According to the text, at the end of the story, what is James's reaction to Harlan's fall?
(A) He is extraordinarily happy.
(B) He doesn't care.
(C) He hopes a doctor is nearby.
(D) He wishes it was autumn already.

11H Thinking Creatively

Answer each question below. Don't be afraid to think creatively.

1. Why is it not advised that a voter feel **indifferent** about voting at election time?

    _____

2. Write a creative book title for a story about three **irascible** goblins who journey to New York City.

    _____

3. Rewrite this sentence using synonyms: He **disdained gullible** kids.

    _____

4. What's scarier: an **onslaught** of bees or the extinction of bees (and the death of all flowers)?

    _____

adept / clarify / connoisseur / disdain / excerpt / gullible / indifferent / irascible / onslaught / profound / pseudonym / pungent / renounce / sage / sleek

5.   Finish this sentence: That car is so **sleek** you could...

_____

Word Breakdown

Other than meaning "wise" or "a wise person," *sage* is also a type of herb in the mint family. Interestingly, the two *sages* come from different roots. The *sage* that means wise comes from the Latin *sapere*, "to have good taste." Apparently you are wise if you have good taste. Originally, the word was used to refer to the "Seven Sages" – seven dudes in ancient Greece who people visited for advice.

The herb *sage* comes from the Latin *salvus*, which means "healthy." Apparently, in old England, people used to use sage to keep their teeth clean and to relieve sore gums. The rapper Sage Francis probably chose his pseudonym after the "wise man" meaning of the word. "Parsley Francis" just doesn't have the same ring to it.

Unit 12 - Southern Ladies

12A Introduction

The Civil War was full of spies. After all, most people in the Confederacy had friends or family in the North, and most people in the Union had friends in the South. If a spy could get information about the other side's troop movements, it could mean the difference between victory and defeat. These spies risked their lives just like the soldiers. Some of them were women.

One of the most important spies was a woman named Elizabeth Van Lew. She lived in Richmond, Virginia, the capital of the Confederacy, and she ran a spy ring of twelve people. One of these people was Mary Bowser, an ex-slave who Van Lew had freed. Van Lew was able to get Bowser a job in the house of Jefferson Davis, the President of the Confederacy. In his house, he and his generals discussed strategies, and Bowser would listen. She'd pass the information to Van Lew who passed it on to General Ulysses S. Grant. Without a doubt, Mary Bowser and Elizabeth Van Lew helped the Union win the war.

12B Song Lyrics

This is the story of two ladies, one black the other white,
Who, during the Civil War, both worked as spies.
They fought for the Union against the South,
Not on battlefields, but from within the house.
Mary and Elizabeth, listen up...

Mary Bowser was born a slave,
This young black girl was strong and brave.
A white girl, Van Lew, Elizabeth,
Was **eccentric**, they called her "Crazy Bet."
She had a sunny **disposition** and a heart of gold,
At a time when humans were bought and sold.
She freed Mary from slave's chains,
And things would never be the same.

To make an **analogy,** or comparison:
She brought life like the air to some.
To improve and **enhance** the life of Mary,
Elizabeth sent her to school in Philly.
After a **stint** at the school, a little bit of time,
She had learned to read and write, line by line.
This was the **epoch**, or period of time,
When Jefferson Davis ruled the South side.

This is for my Southern Ladies, you feel me?

Mary had dark skin like Miles Davis,
She got a job in the house of Jefferson Davis.
She was one of the **principal** spies,
One of the most important humans for the Union.
She was **articulate**, good with the words,

analogy / articulate / cache / convey / crucial / decipher / disposition / eccentric / endeavor / enhance / epoch / ferret / trepidation / stint / principal

But she played dumb, and overheard
The **crucial** and important plans
About where Southern soldiers would take a stand.

She would discover and **ferret** out the details,
They ignored her like, "Who's this dumb female?"
When generals left out maps and plans,
Mary **endeavored** and tried to remember them.
She found out about a **cache** of weapons,
A hiding spot where they kept the cannons.
That afternoon as she hung her laundry,
She hung clothes that were codes for the army.

Elizabeth would walk by, see two socks and a vest,
That meant the Southern armies were marching to the west.
You want to know the rest,
And what's next?
She **deciphered** the codes from the clothes,
Without fear or **trepidation**.
The clothes conveyed and communicated information
That for Ulysses S. Grant probably saved him.

Hook

12C Words Defined

Below you'll find each vocabulary word that was used in the song. Each word is followed by the part of speech, a simple definition and a meaningful sentence. Some words will also have synonyms, antonyms and other forms of the word listed.

1. analogy (noun) a similarity or comparison between two things

My biology teacher made an *analogy* between the human heart and a pump.
Other forms: When two things are *analogous* (adj.), they are related in some way.

2. articulate (adj) said or expressed clearly, or someone who is capable of clear expression

The principal was looking for *articulate* students to make daily announcements over the school intercom.
Other forms: *Articulate* can also be a verb meaning "to pronounce clearly," as in: The doctor tried to delicately *articulate* to the parents that their child was terminally ill.

3. cache (noun) a secret supply

The burglar never found our *cache* of rare coins hidden in the floor.
Synonyms: hiding place, stash, stockpile

4. convey (verb) to transmit information or transport something

The teachers tried to *convey* to Tyler's parents that he was failing all six of his classes.

5. crucial (adj) extremely important or essential

Locating the plane crash site was a *crucial* step in the recovery of the dead passengers.

6. decipher (verb) to decode, figure out, or solve

Some investigators have to *decipher* secret codes in notes intentionally left behind by serial killers.
Antonyms: to scramble, confuse, encode

7. disposition (noun) state of mind, mood or spirit

Natalie had not taken a nap and her *disposition* reflected that.

8. eccentric (adj) strange; not behaving normally

She was *eccentric* all right; she made her clothes out of grass and hay.
Other forms: An *eccentric* (noun) is someone who is *eccentric*.

9. endeavor (verb) to attempt or try

The chefs constantly *endeavor* to keep the food from spoiling by keeping it in the refrigerator until needed.
Other forms: *Endeavor* can also be a noun meaning "an attempt or effort," as in: The skydiver made an *endeavor* to land on both legs in the middle of the arena.

10. enhance (verb) to intensify or magnify

The photographer tried to *enhance* the model's natural beauty by adding softer lights around her face and a fan to blow her hair back.
Synonyms: improve, upgrade
Other forms: Bert made an *enhancement* (noun) to his house by adding on a game room loft and another bathroom.

11. epoch (noun) a time period marked by distinctive events

The treaty ushered in an *epoch* of peace and goodwill.
Synonyms: time, period, era

12. ferret (verb) to discover or search out

Janet is going to try to *ferret* out a candy vending machine in the vegetable canning plant.
Synonyms: extract, unearth, uncover
Other forms: A *ferret* (noun) is "a small, domesticated animal," as in: It is illegal to have a *ferret* as a pet in some states.

13. trepidation (noun) fear or alarm

He approached the scene of the car accident with much *trepidation*.

analogy / articulate / cache / convey / crucial / decipher / disposition / eccentric / endeavor / enhance / epoch / ferret / trepidation / stint / principal

14. stint (noun) a period of time spent doing something

Robin did a short *stint* as a lion trainer with the circus.

15. principal (adj) of first or highest importance

Vinny's *principal* reason for going back home was to get his baseball glove for practice.
Other forms: *Principal* is also a noun meaning "the head or leader of an organization," especially the leader of a school.

12D Fix the Mistake

Each of the sentences below has a mistake. The wrong vocabulary words have been used, so the sentences don't make sense. Rewrite each sentence using the correct vocabulary word from this unit.

1. Although she was shy, she was extremely **crucial** when she spoke in front of a group of people.

   _____

2. I was happy to find my little brother's **epoch** of Halloween candy in the back of his closet.

   _____

3. Frank usually has a sunny **analogy**, but today he looked upset.

   _____

4. Egyptian hieroglyphics can only be **conveyed** by trained archaeologists.

   _____

5. Patti tried to **ferret** her report on bears by typing it and drawing a colorful picture on the cover.

   _____

6. Unbelievably, the opera singer had done a short **trepidation** as a pro boxer.

   _____

7. The **eccentric** reason for canceling the field trip was a lack of funds, but it was also a hassle to organize.

   _____

8. I **conveyed** to build a castle in the sand, but the waves soon washed it away.

   _____

9. To help us understand the inner workings of a cell, our teacher made a clever **cache** between it and our classroom.

   _____

10. The doctor tried to **enhance** the seriousness of my illness by giving me a book to read on the disease.

   _____

11. Evil pirates **articulated** out buried treasure from several different places on the island.

   _____

12. The movie marked a new **disposition** in filmmaking: the golden age.

   _____

13. Dana thought it was **principal** that she tell her boyfriend that her parents were extremely religious and overprotective.

   _____

14. Vicky approached the roller coaster for the first time with incredible **stint**.

   _____

15. Whenever Gerald answered a question correctly in class, he did a(n) **decipher** dance, which consisted of him twirling rapidly.

   _____

12E Pick the Winner

Circle the word that best fits into the sentence. Then write a sentence below that uses the word you didn't pick in a meaningful way.

1. Diego had a **(disposition OR cache)** of sharpened pencils in his desk.

2. _____

3. I feel extreme **(analogy OR trepidation)** toward spiders because I was bit by a black widow as a child.

4. _____

5. Before becoming an actor, Jake did a short **(stint OR endeavor)** as a waiter at a restaurant that was frequented by celebrities.

6. _____

7.   The student council is hoping to **(enhance OR articulate)** the cafeteria with vending machines, microwaves, and a soft serve ice cream machine.

8.   _____

9.   It was **(eccentric OR crucial)** that the air traffic controller got a certain number of hours of sleep before reporting to work.

10.   _____

12F Draw the Relationships

In each grouping of eight words below, draw straight lines between the synonyms (words that mean similar things) and squiggly lines between any antonyms (words that mean nearly opposite things). Every word should have at least one line connected to it. Some may have more.

1
articulate   pronounce clearly
analogy   stash
keep in place   comparison
          cache   convey

2
          decipher   scramble
crucial   essential
disposition   mood
          normal   eccentric

3
          time period   enhance
attempt   ferret
endeavor   make worse
          search for   epoch

4
          period of time   relate
principal   convey
trepidation   most important
          stint   fright

12G Understanding What You Read

Read the passage below. Then answer the questions.

Mary Bowser felt an overwhelming sense of <u>trepidation</u> as she crept into Jefferson Davis' office. Her breath quickly became heavy and shallow, all at the same time. As a servant in the house of the President of the Confederacy, she knew that if she was caught stealing <u>crucial</u> information, she would most certainly be put to death.

She <u>endeavored</u> to calm herself. After all, this wasn't her first time stealing secrets. She had been doing it for weeks. Already, during her <u>stint</u> at Davis' house, she had been able to <u>convey</u> all kinds of plans - troop movements, supply lists and strategies - to her friend and former owner Elizabeth Van Lew. It was Elizabeth who was taking the secrets and <u>conveying</u> the information to the Union army commanders. Mary thought about Elizabeth and how good she was at spying. The fact that everyone thought she was crazy and <u>eccentric</u> made Elizabeth a great spy. People assumed she was just weird, and left her alone. In fact, people also assumed things about Mary. They assumed she couldn't read and that she was too dumb to understand maps. That's why Jefferson Davis and his generals would leave out important maps and documents where Mary could see them.

Mary <u>ferreted</u> through the office and desk, looking for information that would be helpful to the Union. Searching through the papers in Davis' desk, she wondered if the war would be over soon. She picked up a piece of paper and held it to the light. This was it - the <u>principal</u> piece of strategy she was looking for!

She gasped, and then quickly quieted herself down. She knew she would have to maintain an even <u>disposition</u> if she was going to get out of the house without giving herself away. Mary took a deep breath, rolled the fragile document into her overcoat, and stepped out the door.

1. When Mary entered Jefferson Davis' office, she felt
(A) great
(B) excited
(C) scared
(D) like she was going to be sick

2. The Confederate leader would leave crucial documents around the house because
(A) they were lazy
(B) they wanted them cleaned up
(C) they were useless anyway
(D) they didn't think Mary could understand them

3. Mary tries to keep an "even disposition" in order to
(A) trick Elizabeth
(B) pretend she was a Confederate general
(C) not call attention to herself
(D) not drop the document

4. Mary's and Elizabeth's actions could be considered
(A) lucky
(B) boring
(C) risky
(D) funny

5. This passage is an example of
(A) mystery
(B) fantasy
(C) fiction
(D) realistic fiction

12H Thinking Creatively

Answer each question below. Don't be afraid to think creatively.

1.   How would you **convey** to a teacher that you disagree with a grade you received?

_____

2.   If you could leave any message for citizens of the future to find and **decipher**, what would it be?

_____

3.   If you could divide your life into **epochs**, how many would there be and what would you title them?

_____

4.   Describe a TV show called *Ferreting Out Criminals*.

_____

5.   What is your **principal** reason for getting an education?

_____

Word Breakdown

As you might have guessed, *principal* comes from the same root as *prince*. A prince is either a non-ruling member of a royal family (who is in line to be king), or is another word for a royal ruler. The word *prince* comes from two interesting Latin roots: *primus* and *capere*. *Primus* means "first" (think of a nice *prime* rib steak or the word *primary*). *Capere* means "to take" (think *capture*). So someone in ancient Rome combined *primus* and *capere* to somehow make *prince*: the "first taker." Apparently, a *prince* gets to take things first.

The word *principal* comes directly from this idea of "first," and thus means first in importance. The *principal* at your school is first in importance there, and the *principal* reason you go to school is to learn. Don't confuse *principal* with *principle* "a basic truth," though the roots are the same.

Unit 13 - Harrison Bergeron

13A Introduction

The year was 2081, and everyone was finally equal. That is the first line in a short story by Kurt Vonnegut called "Harrison Bergeron." First published in 1961, the story asks an important question: Do we really want to create a society where everyone is equal? What would the government have to do in order to make everyone truly equal?

13B Song Lyrics

I used to have a **flair** for writing rhymes,
A natural talent for crafting lines.
But then they issued a **decree** to the people,
An order that stated we were all equal.
All across the nation we gave it an **ovation**,
We stood up and clapped, till they noticed that
Not everyone could stand up and clap like us,
So they weighed us down and kept us handcuffed.

The weights were a **hindrance** to our movements,
They held us back, so we're equal now.
They **instituted** and set up new rules that
Made pretty kids ugly, and skinny guys fat.
Then they took away and **confiscated**
The books; it was not debated.
So that we'd remember, they built a statue that
Commemorated the day we became the same.

*Are you close or **aloof** to the daily news?*
Do you know what society is doing to you?
Do you know about the wars we wage, the rise of AIDS,
The price we pay to make our lives this way?

This girl Holly probably was a **prodigy**,
So smart she won nine weeks straight on Jeopardy.
I called up the cops, I was feeling jealous,
I said we need to make Holly the same as the others.
It's necessary and **imperative**,
Right now she's the brightest girl that ever lived.
She's not my relative, you better give her a **sedative,**
Some medicine to calm her down, that'll settle it.

I used to be a dedicated and **avid** runner,
They put a chain around my leg and added another.
They made me stop and **desist**, the cops came quick,
They had to make sure that I run with a limp.
Now I'm clumsy and **ungainly**,
And you'll get two years in prison if you unchain me.
They **encroached** upon our rights, took them gradually,

Is this how equality has to be?

Hook

13C Words Defined

Below you'll find each vocabulary word that was used in the song. Each word is followed by the part of speech, a simple definition and a meaningful sentence. Some words will also have synonyms, antonyms and other forms of the word listed.

1. aloof (adj) uninterested or distant

Henry was so *aloof* that he didn't realize that the actor he had idolized for five years was standing right next to him.
Synonyms: detached, distant, disdainful
Other forms: You can also use *aloof* as an adverb: He stood *aloof*.

2. avid (adj) enthusiastic and eager

Melissa was an *avid* bicyclist and sometimes rode over thirty miles a day.
Synonyms: devoted, ardent, voracious

3. commemorate (verb) to honor the memory of

We will *commemorate* the victims of September eleventh with a statue.
Synonyms: to memorialize, pay tribute, to revere

4. confiscate (verb) to use authority to take possession of private property

At the airport, the security agents will *confiscate* any items that could be used as a weapon.
Synonyms: seize, commandeer

5. decree (noun) an authoritative order or decision

The presidential *decree* to release the prisoners was on the President's desk, waiting to be signed.
Synonyms: an act, mandate
Other forms: *Decree* is also a verb meaning "to command or to issue," as in: I *decree* that all students who wear hats in the classroom will receive a detention.

6. desist (verb) to stop doing something

I know you love to yell, but you better *desist* when the teacher comes back.
Synonyms: cease

7. encroach (verb) to advance beyond usual limits

Sometimes I feel like my twin sister tries to encroach on my side of the bedroom with all of her belongings.
Synonyms: to invade, overstep, trespass

8. flair (noun) a natural talent or ability; style

James had a *flair* for taking photos and arranging them attractively in scrapbooks.
Synonyms: gift, talent, aptness
Antonyms: inability, limitation

9. hindrance (noun) something that holds you back

The baseball player's newly broken arm was a *hindrance* to him pitching in any more games for the remainder of the season.
Synonyms: encumbrance, obstacle, restraint
Other forms: A *hindrance hinders* (verb) you.

10. imperative (adj) necessary, required, critical

It is *imperative* to study for your driver's test to ensure that you pass.
Other forms: Imperative is also a noun meaning "a command," as in: The lieutenant gave an *imperative* for all the soldiers to drop and complete fifty push-ups.

11. institute (verb) to establish or begin

The school administration is going to *institute* many new rules because of the increase in misbehavior among the student body.
Other forms: Something established is an *institution* (noun), while an *institute* (noun) is "an organization for the promotion of a specific cause".

12. ovation (noun) loud, prolonged applause

Mr. Costello received a standing *ovation* after he was recognized for saving three children from drowning.
Synonyms: acclaim, applause

13. prodigy (noun) a child with an extraordinary talent or ability

Steven was considered a musical *prodigy* at the age of four because he could play Mozart from memory.
Synonyms: child genius, phenomenon

14. sedative (adj) calming or soothing

The *sedative* music helped to calm the crying baby
Other forms: A *sedative* (noun) "a soothing medication," will *sedate* (verb) or calm a person.

15. ungainly (adj) awkward, clumsy

Frank was so *ungainly* that he tripped over everything all the time.
Synonyms: blundering, uncoordinated, klutzy
Antonyms: graceful, skillful, coordinated

aloof / avid / commemorate / confiscate / decree / desist / encroach / flair / hindrance / imperative / institute / ovation / prodigy / sedative / ungainly

13D Fix the Mistake

Each of the sentences below has a mistake. The wrong vocabulary words have been used, so the sentences don't make sense. Rewrite each sentence using the correct vocabulary word from this unit.

1. After he hit his third home run of the game, the crowd gave him a standing **sedative**.

   _____

2. In honor of the earthquake survivors, each one will get a plaque to **institute** their bravery.

   _____

3. The honors students are such **aloof** readers that they've read every book in the classroom library.

   _____

4. Her cell phone rang so much during the movie that the usher had to **encroach** it.

   _____

5. The committee wrote up a(n) **hindrance** that made the beautiful parkland safe from future construction.

   _____

6. It is rare to see a(n) **imperative** model on the fashion runway: They rarely trip.

   _____

7. Janine had such a strong **prodigy** for baking cakes that the local bakery hired her at the age of sixteen.

   _____

8. We had to **confiscate** from hitchhiking following the serial killings.

   _____

9. Having crutches was such a big **decree** to getting up and down the stairs.

   _____

10. Fred was so **ungainly** that he didn't remove his hat during the national anthem at the ball game, even when everyone around him was doing it.

    _____

11. Most of our family thinks my brother is a musical **ovation** because he can play six
     different instruments at the age of four.

     _____

12. The principal **commemorated** a strange new rule that girls could not wear skirts to
     school on Tuesdays.

     _____

13. I begged the doctor to prescribe some kind of **flair** for my grandmother's increasing anxiety.

     _____

14. It was **avid** that the couple was not late for their dinner reservation, because they'd lose it.

     _____

15. So many new housing communities are starting to **desist** on the natural habitat of black bears.

     _____

13E Pick the Winner

*Circle the word that best fits into the sentence. Then write a sentence below that uses the word you
didn't pick in a meaningful way.*

1. Every night when the tide comes in, I feel like the ocean is **(encroaching OR confiscating)**
    on my waterfront property.

2. _____

3. Einstein was most likely a mathematical **(prodigy OR hindrance)** for his time.

4. _____

5. There were so many girls in the house that their dad **(commemorated OR instituted)**
    a five-minute time limit on the phone.

6. _____

7. Ben had a **(flair OR decree)** for taking care of injured animals.

8. _____

9. The applause was so loud from the **(ovation OR sedative)** that the baby started to cry.

10. _____

aloof / avid / commemorate / confiscate / decree / desist / encroach / flair / hindrance / imperative / institute / ovation / prodigy / sedative / ungainly

13F Draw the Relationships

In each grouping of eight words below, draw straight lines between the synonyms (words that mean similar things) and squiggly lines between any antonyms (words that mean nearly opposite things). Every word should have at least one line connected to it. Some may have more.

1

pronouncement
avid
memorialize
enthusiastic
commemorate
seize
confiscate
decree

2

encroach
desist
natural talent
hindrance
trespass
obstacle
stop
flair

3

institute
imperative
child genius
prodigy
optional
boos
begin
ovation

4

ungainly
sedative
graceful
calming
aloof
detached
eager
avid

13G Understanding What You Read

Read the passage below. Then answer the questions.

The crowd of teenagers and parents in the hotel conference room gave the speaker a standing <u>ovation</u>. The speaker, a man who had spent the last eleven years playing professional basketball, had given an inspiring speech on the importance of hard work. He had talked about how staying in school was <u>imperative</u> to his success. He had discussed how crucial it was for people with money to give back to those in need.

Mike stood in the crowd, not believing he was in the same room as his hero, Stephon Marbury. He had studied Marbury's success, from his days as a young basketball <u>prodigy</u> from Coney Island, through his college career at Georgia Tech and on to the pros. Mike had always been inspired by the way Marbury had never allowed his setbacks in school be a <u>hindrance</u> to his goal of playing in the NBA. Even though some people downplayed it, Mike loved the way his hero played with real <u>flair</u> - sometimes flashy, sometimes quick, but always entertaining. Mike would often argue about Marbury's playing ability with people, and would usually win because he had all of Marbury's stats memorized.

Most interesting was Marbury's new venture. He had started a line of footwear. On the surface, there didn't seem to be anything weird about that: Lots of NBA players had sneaker deals with Nike, Reebok, and Adidas. But Marbury told the crowd what made his shoes different: They were priced at $14.98 a pair. Someone in the audience asked if they were "cheap shoes that would fall apart." Marbury turned to the kid and said, "I'll be wearing a pair of the shoes every game I play in the NBA. If they can hold up on the court, they can hold up in a high school."

Mike told his father he'd be right back and went to the bathroom. As he washed his hands, he turned toward the door; with so much on his mind, he was kind of <u>aloof</u>. He didn't realize a tall man had entered the bathroom until they nearly collided. Mike lifted his head and murmured, "Excuse me, sir."

Only when the voice fell down upon him did Mike realize who he'd run into. "That's alright, little man."

"Oh, wow," Mike stammered. "I'm an <u>avid</u> fan." He stammered out a few more sentences before walking out the door to where his father waited.

"Pops, guess what!"

1. Which character's actions does the narrator follow most carefully?
(A) Stephon Marbury's
(B) Mike's
(C) Mike's pop's
(D) the hotel staff

2. According to the passage, the difference between Marbury's line of shoes and most others is that they
(A) are less popular than other shoes
(B) are more affordable
(C) look cooler
(D) will fall apart faster

3. Why does Mike act aloof in the bathroom?
(A) He's distracted.
(B) He's upset.
(C) He's amazed that Marbury would single him out.
(D) He wants a pair of those special shoes.

4. When the narrator notes that Stephon Marbury plays with "flair," it means that
(A) he has limitations
(B) he has a natural ability
(C) he plays in special sneakers
(D) his hair is on fire

5. In the passage, Stephon Marbury tells the crowd that people who are fortunate
(A) should invest wisely
(B) should create a line of affordable shoes and clothes
(C) should spend time with those they love
(D) should give money back to the poor

13H Thinking Creatively

Answer each question below. Don't be afraid to think creatively.

1.   How does the government **encroach** upon your rights?

   _____

2.   What person would you **commemorate** with a holiday?

   _____

3.   What is **imperative** for every person to do?

   _____

4.   What type of show would be called *America's Most Aloof People* be?

   _____

5.   Would you rather be normal, or an **ungainly prodigy**? Why?

   _____

Word Breakdown

Aloof is a word that comes to us from sailors. The *a* in *aloof* is from Latin and means "toward" (think *afoot* or *ashore*). The *loof* is Middle English for "windward position," which is what a boat wants – to have the wind at a good angle. If a ship were sailing near rocks, a sea captain might give out an order to keep the boat *aloof*, meaning keep it sailing toward the wind, which would prevent the wind from sending it to the rocks. Thus, *aloof* came to mean "at a distance." Now the word is often used to mean "out of it." If someone says our President is aloof, it's not a compliment.

Unit 14 - THE BATTLE

14A Introduction

Rap battles are an important part of hip-hop. It's not a violence thing. It's a competition thing: Who's got the better rhymes? Who's got the punch lines that hit harder? Who's got the funnier metaphors? Well, Trajik and B pick up their mics to throw down on this track. Who do you think wins?

14B Song Lyrics

I'm the best class, I'm **elite**,
From Shakespeare to Snoop Dogg, they rhyme with me.
I've got a **glut** of tight rhymes, an oversupply,
You're over easy, man, you're going to get fried.
And when the battle's done, you'll feel a **pang** of regret,
A sudden feeling, you can't hang with me yet.
You're too **disgruntled**, fed up with life,
I'm like laundry that shrinks, yes, I'm that tight.

You can attack and **assail** me with your words,
But I have a force field for nouns and verbs.
I did this rap first, I'm the **pioneer**,
Call me chopping onion, I'll make you cry a tear.
I don't decay, I'm **durable,** I will last long,
You're sad like when my pet gerbil passed on.
Your style is Wal-Mart, I know where you bought it,
My flow is unusual, it's so **exotic**.

You get honey-glazed, slow-roasted like chicken,
I rule here, I have the **jurisdiction**.
I have skills, man, I'm **proficient**.
If you can't handle the heat, get out of the kitchen.
Is you Dr. Seuss? Your rhymes are simple, kid.
My lines are complex and, yes, **intricate**.
You can't understand, I'm far too deep,
I'm filet mignon, you're Chef-Boy-R-Dee, you see?

Your logic is **porous**, it has holes in it,
You smell like a skunk died with mold in it.
If you thought you'd win, well, something's gone **awry**,
Gone off course, you keep asking why.
This is not small talk, it's not **banter**,
My style is felt from Canada to Atlanta.
I'll diss you in a jiffy, keep it brief and make it **pithy**,
Your whole wardrobe probably cost a dollar-fifty.

14C Words Defined

Below you'll find each vocabulary word that was used in the song. Each word is followed by the part of speech, a simple definition and a meaningful sentence. Some words will also have synonyms,

assail / awry / banter / disgruntled / durable / elite / exotic / glut / intricate / jurisdiction / pang / pioneer / pithy / porous / proficient

antonyms and other forms of the word listed.

1. assail (verb) to violently attack or assault

In fourth grade, a bully used to *assail* Jorge for being short until he grew five inches over the summer.
Other forms: An *assailant* (noun) is a person who attacks someone.

2. awry (adverb) or (adj) turned or twisted; gone wrong

The wedding plans went *awry* when the bride did not show up at the chapel.

3. banter (noun) light talk; witty remarks

She was pretty, but her constant *banter* was driving me crazy; I need some real conversation.

4. disgruntled (adj) grumpy; dissatisfied and sulky

The *disgruntled* baseball player screamed and kicked dirt on the umpire.
Synonyms: unhappy, annoyed, irritable
Other forms: You can *disgruntle* (verb) someone if you make him unhappy.

5. durable (adj) able to stand up to wear and tear; lasting a while

Farmer Jenkins installed *durable* fencing around the pigs to replace the wood posts they had chewed up.
Synonyms: sturdy, reliable
Antonyms: fragile, flimsy, cheap

6. elite (adj) best or first class

The *elite* members of American society often attend Ivy League schools.
Synonyms: aristocratic
Other forms: *Elite* can also be a noun meaning a person who is of a high class.

7. exotic (adj) strange or foreign in character

Stacie always wears the most *exotic* clothing; she even owns a burka.

8. glut (noun) an excessive amount; too much

Due to the small number of people at the birthday party, there was a *glut* of cake leftover.
Antonyms: shortage

9. intricate (adj) complex

Every Halloween, there is an *intricate* corn maze that is fun for us to walk through at night.
Antonyms: simple

10. jurisdiction (noun) power, authority or territory

Although the murder case was out of Officer Brazelton's *jurisdiction*, he continued to investigate.

11. pang (noun) a sudden sharp feeling

A *pang* of hunger took hold of me in the middle of my math test, so I couldn't concentrate on my calculations.
Synonyms: ache, twinge

12. pioneer (noun) someone who settles in a land first or who opens up new areas of research

Dr. E was a *pioneer* in the scientific community as the first doctor to seriously study pimples.

13. pithy (adj) brief but full of meaning; to the point

Marvin was famous for his *pithy* responses in history class because he hated the sound of his own voice.
Antonyms: long-winded

14. porous (adj) full of holes or pores

Our tent was so cheap that its *porous* fabric meant we got soaking wet from the rain.
Antonyms: watertight
Other forms: *Pores* (noun) are little holes: You sweat out of the *pores* in your skin.

15. proficient (adj) skilled

Nick was a *proficient* swimmer and had no problem passing the swim test.
Synonyms: accomplished, competent

14D Fix the Mistake

Each of the sentences below has a mistake. The wrong vocabulary words have been used, so the sentences don't make sense. Rewrite each sentence using the correct vocabulary word from this unit.

1.   The mugger **bantered** the old lady and ran away with her purse.

_____

2.   Some **durable** customers complained to the restaurant manager and refused to pay their bill.

_____

3.   The plans to get to the ballgame all went **proficiently** when the bridge collapsed due to the mudslide.

_____

4.   Some celebrities think they are so **intricate** that they have chauffeurs take them everywhere.

_____

5.   After the holidays, there is always a(n) **pang** of new coffee mugs in the teachers' lounge.

   _____

6.   Grandma's stories were never **porous**; each one lasted over an hour.

   _____

7.   Lewis and Clark were famous **glut**, exploring land for the government that hadn't been explored before.

   _____

8.   I had felt normal all day, but the moment I saw Jenny in the hall, I felt a sharp **jurisdiction** of love.

   _____

9.   My new raincoat was so **pithy** that I took it back to the store and asked for a refund.

   _____

10. There aren't usually heavy conversations at parties; it's mostly just **pioneer**.

   _____

11. One of the most **elite** types of rainforest birds is on display at the zoo's entrance.

   _____

12. Jennifer was such a(n) **exotic** writer that, despite her young age, many of her short stories were published in the local magazine.

   _____

13. At the museum, the ancient mummy was encased in a very **disgruntled** glass box to protect it.

   _____

14. The spider's web was so **awry** that it must have taken a week to build.

   _____

15. The crooked cop was giving tickets and citing people out of his **glut**.

   _____

14E Pick the Winner

Circle the word that best fits into the sentence. Then write a sentence below that uses the word you didn't pick in a meaningful way.

1.   The burglary went **(awry OR assail)** when the robbers passed through an invisible laser and sounded the alarms.

2.   _____

3.   The **(disgruntled OR porous)** weatherman gave an incorrect forecast for the week because he was angry at losing his job.

4.   _____

5.   Mark's **(porous OR pithy)** class presentation on caring for pets made all of us walk our dogs more.

6.   _____

7.   At the parent-teacher conference, my mom was pleased when the teacher told her I was more than **(proficient OR intricate)** at reading and writing.

8.   _____

9.   Everyone in the library knew I was experiencing **(pangs OR jurisdictions)** of hunger because my stomach was growling so loudly.

10.   _____

14F Draw the Relationships

In each grouping of eight words below, draw straight lines between the synonyms (words that mean similar things) and squiggly lines between any antonyms (words that mean nearly opposite things). Every word should have at least one line connected to it. Some may have more.

1
assail   chit-chat   awry   disgruntled

assault   annoyed   banter   gone wrong

2
durable   bizarre   exotic   glut

best   elite   flimsy   a small portion

3

intricate

jurisdiction

ache

pang

complex

pioneer

latecomer

power

....

4

porous

able

pithy

assail

attack

long-winded

waterproof

proficient

14G Understanding What You Read

Read the passage below. Then answer the questions.

There is music from all over the world, and much of it uses drums. The drum adds rhythm. It keeps the beat. It even makes music easier to dance to. But the drum has an extra special place in Pueblo culture. They say that the beat of the drum is tied to the beat of the heart.

One of the holidays for Taos Pueblo Indians is a special feast day on January 6. On this day, the village gathers for a buffalo dance, as they have done for hundreds of years.

The day starts with a delicious meal. There isn't a <u>glut</u> of food, but there's enough for everyone. During the meal, there is much <u>banter,</u> just as there is at any other meal. After the meal, however, the women clear the table and the men bring out the family drum. While one member of the family beats the drum, others sing songs. The songs they sing are Taos Pueblo and Apache round dance songs. These songs date back to the 1800s and have been passed down orally from generation to generation.

Between songs, the drummer pauses and closes his eyes. This isn't a sign that something has gone awry. He is thinking of which song they should sing next, and he closes his eyes to concentrate. In his mind, he travels back through his life to all of the people he has met and the songs he has learned. Songs come to his memory as if carried on a breeze.

While the people in the room wait for him to choose, no one looks <u>disgruntled</u>. In fact, the pause between songs becomes a part of the rhythm of the celebration. The songs they sing are a little more <u>exotic</u> than the tunes you hear on the radio, but they are beautiful melodies. The songs and the people are what make the holiday so special for the Pueblo people.

1. When in time does the passage seem to take place?
(A) recently
(B) long, long ago
(C) in the early 1800s
(D) around 1492

2. Which of the following sentences best describes the actions of the Pueblo people during the meal?
(A) They remain silent.
(B) They eat very quickly.
(C) They sing songs.
(D) They chat with each other.

3. Which of the following is NOT mentioned in the text to describe drums?
(A) Drums are one of the loudest instruments.
(B) Drums are used in all kinds of world music.
(C) Drums add rhythm to music.
(D) Drums make music easier to dance to.

4. The phrase "songs come to his memory as if carried on a breeze" probably means that the songs
(A) make him feel cold
(B) are hard to remember
(C) come easily
(D) make him feel good

5. The people in the room hear the pauses between songs and react by
(A) booing
(B) waiting patiently
(C) cheering
(D) eating more food

14H Thinking Creatively

Answer each question below. Don't be afraid to think creatively.

1. Describe why you would rather be considered a **pioneer** or **elite**.

    _____

2. How might you creatively but legally acquire a **glut** of money?

    _____

3. Write a **pithy** statement about friendship.

    _____

4. Describe a TV show named *Something's Gone Awry!*

    _____

5. As a future parent, what **jurisdiction** will you have over your own children?

    _____

Word Breakdown

The word *disgruntle* kind of sounds like what it means. When you feel *disgruntled* you might grunt – make the sound that a hog makes. In fact, that is where the word comes from. The word combines *dis* (which in this case means "very," but usually means "not") and *gruntle* (which means to grunt). The word *grunt* probably comes from people trying to imitate the sound of a hog, just like the verbs to bark, to caw and to moo.

The word *grumble* means to complain in a low voice or under your breath. If you're *disgruntled*, you might *grumble*. The underground rapper Arecee hasn't gotten rich off the game yet. He raps that he's "becoming disgruntled 'cause life is such a struggle."

Word List *vocab word (unit number)*

Abet (6)
accord (9)
adept (11)
advocate (5)
agile (2)
allot (7)
aloof (13)
amiss (3)
analogy (12)
anarchy (1)
antics (9)
apprehend (10)
ardent (1)
articulate (12)
assail (14)
assimilate (7)
atrocity (6)
attribute (5)
audacious (2)
augment (1)
authority (10)
avail (3)
avid (13)
awry (14)

Balmy (4)
banter (14)
barter (8)
benign (9)
bizarre (3)
blasé (1)
bonanza (9)
bountiful (7)

Cache (12)
capacious (5)
caption (6)
chastise (3)
citadel (4)
cite (9)
clad (4)
clarify (11)
commemorate (13)
component (9)
concept (9)
confiscate (13)
connoisseur (11)
conscientious (10)
conservative (5)
contagious (3)
conventional (7)

convey (12)
crucial (12)
crusade (2)
culminate (3)

Deceptive (7)
decipher (12)
decree (13)
deface (9)
defect (8)
deplore (3)
deploy (6)
desist (13)
desolate (1)
deter (10)
dialect (3)
dire (10)
discern (6)
disdain (11)
disgruntled (14)
dispatch (8)
disposition (12)
doctrine (8)
dub (2)
durable (14)

Eccentric (12)
elite (14)
embargo (8)
embark (1)
encroach (13)
endeavor (12)
enhance (12)
enigma (9)
epoch (12)
era (2)
eventful (10)
evolve (6)
exceptional (2)
excerpt (11)
excruciating (10)
exemplify (6)
exotic (14)

Facilitate (10)
fallacy (4)
fastidious (6)
feasible (6)
fend (1)
ferret (12)
flair (13)
flustered (8)
foreboding (8)

forfeit (5)
formidable (8)
fortify (8)
foster (7)

Gaunt (8)
gingerly (4)
glut (14)
grapple (2)
grope (4)
gullible (11)

Haggard (8)
haven (7)
heritage (2)
hindrance (13)
hover (3)
humane (5)

Imperative (13)
inaugurate (5)
incense (8)
indifferent (11)
infinite (9)
instill (7)
institute (13)
intervene (4)
intricate (14)
inventive (6)
inventory (8)
irascible (11)

Jurisdiction (14)

Languish (10)
legendary (2)
liberal (5)
loll (3)
lucrative (9)
luminous (10)

Memoir (7)
mercenary (4)
mien (2)
millennium (10)
minimize (6)
modify (3)
muse (2)
muster (2)

Onslaught (11)
ornate (7)
ovation (13)
overt (8)

Pang (14)
panorama (1)
perspective (6)
phenomenon (7)
pioneer (14)
pithy (14)
pivotal (2)
plausible (5)
plunder (4)
porous (14)
preposterous (3)
principal (12)
prodigy (13)
proficient (14)
profound (11)
pseudonym (11)
pungent (11)

Rankle (10)
rational (9)
rebuke (6)
reception (1)
recourse (5)
recur (10)
renounce (11)
renown (5)
revenue (4)
rubble (1)
rue (4)

Sage (11)
sedative (13)
serene (9)
servile (5)
shackle (7)
sleek (11)
spontaneous (3)
sporadic (6)
stamina (2)
stance (2)
staple (4)
stint (12)
strident (10)
sublime (7)
subside (3)
succumb (9)
surpass (7)
susceptible (8)
swelter (10)

Tedious (3)
teem (1)
theme (7)

tirade (5)
tract (1)
transition (9)
trepidation (12)
turbulent (4)
tycoon (4)

Ultimate (5)
ungainly (13)

Vice versa (1)
vie (1)
vilify (4)
voracious (6)

Wage (5)
wrangle (1)